THE JUMBO

JEOPARDY!™

QUIZ BOOK

THE JUMBO
JEOPARDY!
QUIZ BOOK

Jeopardy! . . . What Is Quiz Book 1?
Jeopardy! . . . What Is Quiz Book 2?

Quality Paperback Book Club
New York

The Jumbo Jeopardy Quiz Book

JEOPARDY!

™

What Is Quiz Book 1?

JEOPARDY!

2-LETTER WORDS

PEOPLE WITH A HIDDEN AGENDA OFTEN HAVE THIS "TO GRIND"	**$100**	WHAT IS
"COLLECT $200" IF YOU CAN NAME THIS JAPANESE GAME PLAYED WITH BLACK & WHITE COUNTERS ON A CHECKERED BOARD	**$200**	WHAT IS
AS A PREFIX, IT CAN MEAN "NOT INCLUD-ING"; BY ITSELF, IT MEANS "FORMER", LIKE A FORMER SPOUSE	**$300**	WHAT IS
YES, IT'S RUSSIAN FOR YES	**$400**	WHAT IS
"VERY", "WHAT'S YOUR POINT?" OR THE TITLE OF A PETER GABRIEL ALBUM	**$500**	WHAT IS

JEOPARDY!

2-LETTER WORDS

$100	WHAT IS AN AX?	**$100**
$200	WHAT IS GO?	**$200**
$300	WHAT IS EX?	**$300**
$400	WHAT IS DA?	**$400**
$500	WHAT IS SO?	**$500**

JEOPARDY!

KIDDY LIT

IT'S A PARROT, NAMED POLYNESIA, WHO TEACHES THIS DOCTOR THE LANGUAGE OF ANIMALS	**$100**	WHO IS
THE FRONTISPIECE OF THIS ROBERT LOUIS STEVENSON PIRATE BOOK FEATURED A DETAILED MAP	**$200**	WHAT IS
"THE GREAT SWANS SWAM ROUND HIM, STROKING HIM WELCOMINGLY"	**$300**	WHO IS
HE WAS "BAWN AND BRED IN A BRIER-PATCH"	**$400**	WHO IS
THIS BOOK BEGINS WITH THE MOLE "SPRING-CLEANING HIS LITTLE HOME"	**$500**	WHAT IS

JEOPARDY!™

KIDDY LIT

$100 WHO IS DOCTOR (JOHN) DOLITTLE? **$100**

$200 WHAT IS "TREASURE ISLAND"? **$200**

$300 WHO IS THE UGLY DUCKLING? **$300**

$400 WHO IS BRER RABBIT? **$400**

$500 WHAT IS "THE WIND IN THE WILLOWS"? **$500**

JEOPARDY!

ANIMALS ON THE MAP

A 4,083-FOOT-HIGH VERMONT MOUNTAIN IS NAMED FOR THIS CAMEL FEATURE	**$100**	WHAT IS
LOCATED AT THE HEAD OF THE NIAGARA RIVER, IT'S THE SEAT OF NEW YORK'S ERIE COUNTY	**$200**	WHAT IS
"THE WORLD IS NOT ENOUGH" ENDS WITH JAMES BOND & A WOMAN NAMED CHRISTMAS IN THIS EUROPEAN-ASIAN COUNTRY	**$300**	WHAT IS
IN OTHER WORDS, THIS VACATION AREA IN CALIFORNIA'S SAN BERNARDINO MOUNTAINS WOULD BE "LARGE GRIZZLY"	**$400**	WHAT IS
THIS RIVER WINDS ITS WAY THROUGH HELLS CANYON	**$500**	WHAT IS

JEOPARDY!™

ANIMALS ON THE MAP

$100   WHAT IS A (CAMEL'S) HUMP?   **$100**

$200   WHAT IS BUFFALO?   **$200**

$300   WHAT IS TURKEY?   **$300**

$400   WHAT IS BIG BEAR (VALLEY)? (ACCEPT: BIG BEAR LAKE)   **$400**

$500   WHAT IS THE SNAKE RIVER?   **$500**

JEOPARDY!

TRANSPORTATION

THIS ALLITERATIVE TERM FOR A CAR WITH LOW FUEL EFFICIENCY BECAME COMMON IN THE 1970S	$100	WHAT IS
FOUND ON MANY SPORT UTILITY VEHICLES, IT'S A SYSTEM WHERE BOTH AXLES PROVIDE PROPULSION	$200	WHAT IS
TRANSPORT THAT HELPED THE FINNS IN THE 1939-40 WINTER WAR & HELPED FINN MATTI NYKAENEN WIN OLYMPIC GOLD	$300	WHAT ARE
IT WAS CREATED IN 1971 & FORMALLY CALLED THE NATIONAL RAILROAD PASSENGER CORPORATION	$400	WHAT IS
THIS DEVICE INCREASES A JET PLANE'S THRUST BY BURNING EXHAUST GASES	$500	WHAT IS

JEOPARDY!™

TRANSPORTATION

$100 — WHAT IS A GAS GUZZLER? — $100

$200 — WHAT IS 4-WHEEL DRIVE? (ACCEPT: ALL-WHEEL DRIVE) — $200

$300 — WHAT ARE SKIS? — $300

$400 — WHAT IS AMTRAK? — $400

$500 — WHAT IS AN AFTERBURNER? (ACCEPT: TAIL PIPE BURNER) — $500

JEOPARDY!

PEOPLE IN SONG

JIM CROCE'S FIRST NO. 1 HIT WAS ABOUT THIS "BAD BAD" MAN	**$100**	WHO IS
IT'S WHOM THE McCOYS TOLD TO "HANG ON" IN 1965	**$200**	WHO IS
ELTON JOHN HAD A 1975 HIT WITH THIS PSYCHEDELIC BEATLES SONG	**$300**	WHAT IS
SHE WAS "DIRTY" IN THE TITLE OF A SONG FROM MICHAEL JACKSON'S ALBUM "BAD"	**$400**	WHO IS
LOU REED'S SONG ABOUT THIS "SWEET" FEMALE APPEARS ON THE VELVET UNDERGROUND ALBUM "LOADED"	**$500**	WHO IS

9

JEOPARDY!™

PEOPLE IN SONG

$100   WHO IS (BAD BAD) LEROY BROWN?   **$100**

$200   WHO IS SLOOPY?   **$200**

$300   WHAT IS "LUCY IN THE SKY WITH DIAMONDS"?   **$300**

$400   WHO IS DIANA?   **$400**

$500   WHO IS "SWEET JANE"?   **$500**

JEOPARDY!

"LITTLE" WOMEN

NURSERY RHYME CONSUMER OF CURDS & WHEY	**$100**	WHO IS
ONCE CAROLE KING'S BABYSITTER, SHE URGED US TO "DO THE LOCO-MOTION"	**$200**	WHO IS
THIS H.C. ANDERSEN CHARACTER TRIES TO KEEP WARM ON NEW YEAR'S EVE & HAS VISIONS OF HER GRANDMOTHER	**$300**	WHO IS
THIS MISCHIEVOUS GIRL WITH CORKSCREW CURLS APPEARED IN THE SATURDAY EVENING POST FOR OVER 10 YEARS	**$400**	WHO IS
THIS FRANCES HODGSON BURNETT TITLE CHARACTER IS NOT THE FEMALE VERSION OF A SAINT-EXUPERY CHARACTER	**$500**	WHO IS

JEOPARDY!

"LITTLE" WOMEN

$100   WHO IS LITTLE MISS MUFFET? $100

$200   WHO IS LITTLE EVA? $200

$300   WHO IS THE LITTLE MATCH GIRL? $300

$400   WHO IS LITTLE LULU? $400

$500   WHO IS "A LITTLE PRINCESS"? $500

DOUBLE JEOPARDY!

EUROPEAN PAINTERS

THIS PORTRAYER OF PARISIAN NIGHTLIFE WAS DESCENDED FROM THE COUNTS OF TOULOUSE	**$200**	WHO IS
HE COMPLETED HIS PAINTINGS OF "MORN-INGS ON THE SEINE" BEFORE BEGINNING HIS "WATER LILIES"	**$400**	WHO IS
AROUND 1485 THIS FLORENTINE PAINTED "MARS AND VENUS" & "THE BIRTH OF VENUS"	**$600**	WHO IS
YOU MIGHT "SCREAM" WHEN YOU SEE THIS NORWEGIAN'S "SELF-PORTRAIT WITH SKELE-TON ARM"	**$800**	WHO IS
THIS SPANIARD WAS NAMED FIRST COURT PAINTER TO KING CHARLES IV IN 1799	**$1000**	WHO IS

DOUBLE JEOPARDY!

EUROPEAN PAINTERS

$200	WHO IS HENRI DE TOULOUSE-LAUTREC?	**$200**
$400	WHO IS CLAUDE MONET?	**$400**
$600	WHO IS SANDRO BOTTICELLI?	**$600**
$800	WHO IS EDVARD MUNCH?	**$800**
$1000	WHO IS FRANCISCO GOYA?	**$1000**

DOUBLE JEOPARDY!

FUN & GAMES

Clue	Value	Response
THE "CHINESE" FORM OF THIS USES MARBLES RATHER THAN DISKS	$200	WHAT IS
"SHARE A SMILE" BECKY, BARBIE'S FIRST FRIEND WITH A DISABILITY, CAME COMPLETE WITH A PINK ONE OF THESE VEHICLES	$400	WHAT IS
INTRODUCED IN THE 1950s, THIS "MODELING COMPOUND" BEGAN AS A CLEANING PRODUCT FOR WALLPAPER	$600	WHAT IS
THE SECOND HALF OF A SYNONYM FOR TABLE TENNIS, OR THE FIRST SUCCESSFUL VIDEO GAME	$800	WHAT IS
JOHNNY CARSON & EVA GABOR MADE THIS PARTY GAME A HIT WHEN THEY TRIED IT ON TV	$1000	WHAT IS

DOUBLE JEOPARDY!

FUN & GAMES

$200	WHAT IS CHECKERS?	**$200**
$400	WHAT IS A WHEELCHAIR?	**$400**
$600	WHAT IS PLAY-DOH?	**$600**
$800	WHAT IS PONG?	**$800**
$1000	WHAT IS TWISTER?	**$1000**

DOUBLE JEOPARDY!

CLASSIC FOREIGN FILMS

THE UNCUT VERSION OF THIS RUSSIAN EPIC BASED ON A TOLSTOY NOVEL IS MORE THAN 8 HOURS LONG	**$200**	WHAT IS
THIS FILM ALSO KNOWN AS "LES PARAPLUIES DE CHERBOURG" IS THE PERFECT RENTAL FOR A RAINY DAY	**$400**	WHAT IS
WHEN HE WAS LIVING IN ITALY, RICHARD SIMMONS APPEARED IN THE FOOD ORGY SCENE OF THIS DIRECTOR'S FILM "SATYRICON"	**$600**	WHO IS
TOSHIRO MIFUNE STARRED IN THIS DIRECTOR'S EPIC "THRONE OF BLOOD", SORT OF A SAMURAI VERSION OF "MACBETH"	**$800**	WHO IS
"SOLDIER OF ORANGE", A 1977 FILM FROM THIS COUNTRY, MADE RUTGER HAUER AN INTERNATIONAL STAR	**$1000**	WHAT IS

DOUBLE JEOPARDY!

CLASSIC FOREIGN FILMS

$200	WHAT IS "WAR AND PEACE"? (ACCEPT: VOYNA I MIR)	**$200**
$400	WHAT IS "THE UMBRELLAS OF CHERBOURG"?	**$400**
$600	WHO IS (FEDERICO) FELLINI?	**$600**
$800	WHO IS AKIRA KUROSAWA?	**$800**
$1000	WHAT IS THE NETHERLANDS? (ACCEPT: HOLLAND)	**$1000**

DOUBLE JEOPARDY!

U.S. HISTORY

FROM LATIN FOR "PUT AN END TO", THESE REFORMERS LIKE WILLIAM LLOYD GARRISON WANTED TO PUT AN END TO SLAVERY	$200	WHAT ARE
THOROUGHLY RESTORED FOR ITS 100TH BIRTHDAY IN 1986, ITS TORCH WAS RELIT ON JULY 3 THAT YEAR	$400	WHAT IS
ON JULY 2, 1932 FDR SAID, "I PLEDGE MYSELF TO" ONE OF THESE "FOR THE AMERICAN PEOPLE"	$600	WHAT IS
IN 10 MINUTES, A MAY 31, 1889 FLOOD DESTROYED THIS PENNSYLVANIA TOWN & KILLED OVER 2,200 PEOPLE	$800	WHAT IS
IN SEPTEMBER 1847 THIS GENERAL LED THE AMERICAN TROOPS THAT CAPTURED MEXICO CITY	$1000	WHO IS

DOUBLE JEOPARDY!

U.S. HISTORY

$200 | WHAT ARE ABOLITIONISTS? | $200

$400 | WHAT IS THE STATUE OF LIBERTY? | $400

$600 | WHAT IS "NEW DEAL"? | $600

$800 | WHAT IS JOHNSTOWN? | $800

$1000 | WHO IS WINFIELD SCOTT? | $1000

DOUBLE JEOPARDY!

MEET AL GORE

ENLISTING IN 1969, GORE SERVED AS AN ARMY REPORTER IN THIS FOREIGN COUNTRY	**$200**	WHAT IS
THIS FILM STAR SEEN IN "THE FUGITIVE" & "MEN IN BLACK" WAS AL'S ROOMMATE AT HARVARD	**$400**	WHO IS
AUTHOR ERICH SEGAL SAYS OLIVER BARRETT IV IN THIS 1970 NOVEL WAS PARTLY BASED ON AL	**$600**	WHAT IS
AL'S 1992 TREATISE ON THE ENVIRONMENT WAS TITLED THIS "IN THE BALANCE"	**$800**	WHAT IS
THE GORES' OLDEST DAUGHTER, SHE MARRIED A DOCTOR IN 1997	**$1000**	WHO IS

DOUBLE JEOPARDY!

MEET AL GORE

$200	WHAT IS (SOUTH) VIETNAM?	$200
$400	WHO IS TOMMY LEE JONES?	$400
$600	WHAT IS "LOVE STORY"?	$600
$800	WHAT IS EARTH?	$800
$1000	WHO IS KARENNA (GORE SCHIFF)?	$1000

DOUBLE JEOPARDY!

GRAMMAR

Clue	Value	Response
THIS TYPE OF WORD OFTEN ENDS WITH -LY, BUT NOT IN PHRASES LIKE "OFTEN ENDS"	$200	WHAT IS
THE PROHIBITION ON SPLITTING THESE MAY DERIVE FROM THE FACT THAT IN LATIN THEY'RE ONE WORD	$400	WHAT ARE
A CLAUSE THAT MODIFIES A MAIN CLAUSE, OR A TERM FOR A SOLDIER OF LOWER RANK THAN ANOTHER	$600	WHAT IS
SOMETIMES IGNORED IN ENGLISH, IT'S THE MOOD OF HYPOTHETICAL STATEMENTS, AS IN "IF I WERE KING"	$800	WHAT IS
THIS WORD FOR SENTENCES LIKE "YOU'VE GROWN ANOTHER FOOT" COMES FROM LATIN FOR "TO GO AROUND"	$1000	WHAT IS

23

DOUBLE JEOPARDY!

GRAMMAR

$200	WHAT IS AN ADVERB?
$400	WHAT ARE INFINITIVES?
$600	WHAT IS SUBORDINATE?
$800	WHAT IS THE SUBJUNCTIVE?
$1000	WHAT IS AMBIGUOUS? (ACCEPT: AMBIGUITY)

FINAL JEOPARDY!

INVENTORS

HE WAS INDUCTED INTO
THE INVENTORS HALL OF
FAME IN 1997 FOR INVENT-
ING THE SUPERCOMPUTER

WHO IS

FINAL JEOPARDY!

INVENTORS

WHO IS
SEYMOUR CRAY?

JEOPARDY!

HOT DATES

THEN THE WORLD'S LONGEST SUSPENSION BRIDGE, IT OPENED OVER THE EAST RIVER MAY 24, 1883	**$100**	WHAT IS
DELIVERED NOVEMBER 19, 1863, IT LASTED ONLY 2 MINUTES	**$200**	WHAT IS
THIS AL CAPP COMIC STRIP MADE ITS LAST APPEARANCE NOVEMBER 13, 1977	**$300**	WHAT IS
REFERRING TO THE STOCK MARKET CRASH ON OCTOBER 30, 1929, VARIETY RAN THE HEADLINE "WALL ST." DOES THIS	**$400**	WHAT IS
HE WAS LAST REPORTED ALIVE JULY 30, 1975 OUTSIDE A BLOOMFIELD TOWNSHIP, MICH. RESTAURANT	**$500**	WHO IS

JEOPARDY!™

HOT DATES

$100   WHAT IS THE BROOKLYN BRIDGE?   **$100**

$200   WHAT IS THE GETTYSBURG ADDRESS?   **$200**

$300   WHAT IS "LI'L ABNER"?   **$300**

$400   WHAT IS "LAYS AN EGG"?   **$400**

$500   WHO IS JAMES R. HOFFA?   **$500**

28

JEOPARDY!™

POTATOES

THE POTATO ORIGINATED ON THIS CONTINENT, WHERE IT WAS CULTIVATED BY THE INCAS	**$100**	WHAT IS
THE ORIGINAL VERSION OF THIS TOY INCLUDED FACIAL PIECES TO ATTACH TO A REAL SPUD	**$200**	WHAT IS
THE FUNGUS PHYTOPHTHORA INFESTANS CAUSED THIS HISTORIC IRISH TRAGEDY	**$300**	WHAT IS
IN 1853 CHEF GEORGE CRUM INVENTED THIS SNACK AS A JOKE WHEN A CUSTOMER SAID HIS FRIES WERE TOO THICK	**$400**	WHAT ARE
5-LETTER WORD APPLIED TO THE POTATO AS THE OUTGROWTH OF AN UNDERGROUND STEM	**$500**	WHAT IS

JEOPARDY!™

POTATOES

$100 · **WHAT IS SOUTH AMERICA?** · $100

$200 · **WHAT IS MR. POTATO HEAD?** · $200

$300 · **WHAT IS THE (GREAT) (IRISH) POTATO FAMINE? (ACCEPT: BLIGHT)** · $300

$400 · **WHAT ARE POTATO CHIPS?** · $400

$500 · **WHAT IS TUBER?** · $500

JEOPARDY!

WOMEN IN SPORTS

400-METER STAR CATHY FREEMAN WAS THE FIRST OF THESE INDIGENOUS AUSTRALIANS TO WIN A WORLD TRACK GOLD MEDAL	**$100**	WHAT ARE
SHE HAD WON 7 OF 9 GRAND SLAM SINGLES EVENTS WHEN SHE WAS STABBED & WOUNDED IN 1993	**$200**	WHO IS
PAULA NEWBY- FRASER COULD BE CALLED IRONWOMAN FOR WINNING THIS IRON-MAN EVENT 7 TIMES FROM 1986 TO 1994	**$300**	WHAT IS
IN 1997 THIS GYMNAST WHO VAULTED HURT AT THE '96 OLYMPICS WENT TO ISRAEL FOR THE MACCABIAH GAMES	**$400**	WHO IS
IN 1993 MARGE SCHOTT, OWNER OF THIS TEAM, WAS SUSPENDED FOR MAK-ING RACIST REMARKS	**$500**	WHAT ARE

JEOPARDY!

WOMEN IN SPORTS

$100 WHAT ARE ABORIGINES? $100

$200 WHO IS MONICA SELES? $200

$300 WHAT IS THE (IRONMAN) TRIATHLON? $300

$400 WHO IS KERRI STRUG? $400

$500 WHAT ARE THE CINCINNATI REDS? $500

JEOPARDY!

PEOPLE & PLACES

Clue	Value	Response
BAGHDADIS ARE CITIZENS OF THIS COUNTRY; WE DON'T KNOW WHERE THE BAGHMOMMIS LIVE	**$100**	WHAT IS
IT ISN'T INSULTING TO BE CALLED A GOPHER IF YOU LIVE IN THIS "GOPHER STATE"	**$200**	WHAT IS
THESE NOMADS CALL THEMSELVES THE ROM, WHICH MEANS "MAN" OR "HUSBAND" IN THEIR LANGUAGE, ROMANY	**$300**	WHO ARE
THE PEOPLE OF THIS "CONSTITUTION STATE" ARE CALLED NUTMEGS OR NUTMEGGERS	**$400**	WHAT IS
CANADIANS ARE FROM CANADA; CANARIANS ARE FROM THE CANARY ISLANDS, PART OF THIS COUNTRY	**$500**	WHAT IS

33

JEOPARDY!™

PEOPLE & PLACES

$100	WHAT IS IRAQ?	$100
$200	WHAT IS MINNESOTA?	$200
$300	WHO ARE THE GYPSIES?	$300
$400	WHAT IS CONNECTICUT?	$400
$500	WHAT IS SPAIN?	$500

34

JEOPARDY!

LITERARY HODGEPODGE

THIS 1939 STEINBECK NOVEL ABOUT A FAMILY OF MIGRANT WORKERS WON THE PULITZER PRIZE FOR FICTION	**$100**	WHAT IS
WORDSWORTH'S POEM ABOUT HER BEGINS, "HAIL, VIRGIN QUEEN! O'ER MANY AN ENVIOUS BAR TRIUMPHANT..."	**$200**	WHO IS
TITLE CHARACTER WHO SAYS, "I SHALL GROW OLD...AND DREADFUL. BUT THIS PICTURE WILL REMAIN ALWAYS YOUNG"	**$300**	WHO IS
THE MINISTRY OF LOVE, ALSO KNOWN AS MINILUV, MAINTAINS LAW & ORDER IN THIS ORWELL NOVEL	**$400**	WHAT IS
JOHN UPDIKE CHARACTER WHOSE NAME PRECEDES "RUN", "REDUX", "IS RICH" & "AT REST"	**$500**	WHO IS

JEOPARDY!™

LITERARY HODGEPODGE

$100	WHAT IS "THE GRAPES OF WRATH"?	**$100**
$200	WHO IS ELIZABETH I?	**$200**
$300	WHO IS DORIAN GRAY?	**$300**
$400	WHAT IS "1984"?	**$400**
$500	WHO IS RABBIT (ANGSTROM)?	**$500**

JEOPARDY!™

10-LETTER WORDS

Clue		Response
IT'S A STATEMENT OF WHAT A THING IS, & CAN ALSO REFER TO CLEARLY OUTLINED MUSCLES	**$100**	WHAT IS
IN A CRIMINAL TRIAL, IT'S THIS LAWYER'S JOB TO TRY & PROVE THE DEFENDANT GUILTY	**$200**	WHO IS
IT'S EQUAL TO .0394 INCHES	**$300**	WHAT IS
IT'S THE PIGMENT THAT MAKES RED BLOOD CELLS RED	**$400**	WHAT IS
A CREATURE THAT EATS BOTH ANIMALS & PLANTS IS DESCRIBED BY THIS ADJECTIVE	**$500**	WHAT IS

JEOPARDY!

10-LETTER WORDS

$100	WHAT IS DEFINITION?	$100
$200	WHO IS THE PROSECUTOR?	$200
$300	WHAT IS A MILLIMETER?	$300
$400	WHAT IS HEMOGLOBIN?	$400
$500	WHAT IS OMNIVOROUS?	$500

DOUBLE JEOPARDY!

BALLET

Clue	Value	Response
THIS HEROINE'S STEPSISTERS TRY TO SQUEEZE THEIR BIG FEET INTO HER GLASS SLIPPER, BUT THEY DON'T FIT	$200	WHO IS
THIS LATE BALLET STAR OF TARTAR ANCESTRY WAS MARGOT FONTEYN'S BEST-KNOWN PARTNER	$400	WHO IS
THIS TROUPE WAS FIRST ORGANIZED IN MOSCOW IN THE 1770S	$600	WHAT IS
1-WORD TITLE OF AARON COPLAND'S 1942 BALLET INSPIRED BY AMERICAN FOLK TUNES	$800	WHAT IS
THE EROTIC ENDING OF THIS GREAT DANCER'S 1912 BALLET "L'APRES-MIDI D'UN FAUNE" CREATED A SCANDAL	$1000	WHO IS

DOUBLE JEOPARDY!

BALLET

$200	WHO IS CINDERELLA? (ACCEPT: CENDRILLON)
$400	WHO IS RUDOLF NUREYEV?
$600	WHAT IS THE BOLSHOI (BALLET OR THEATER)?
$800	WHAT IS "RODEO"?
$1000	WHO IS VASLAV NIJINSKY?

DOUBLE JEOPARDY!

THAT'S COOL

ONE REVIEW OF THIS 1967 FILM SAID NEWMAN PLAYS "A TOUGH NUT" WHO "REFUSES TO CRACK UNDER PRESSURE"	**$200**	WHAT IS
KRAFT WARNS NOT TO USE THE MICROWAVE TO THAW THIS DESSERT TOPPER, FIRST SOLD NATIONALLY IN 1968	**$400**	WHAT IS
WHILE YOU TWIDDLE YOUR THUMBS, IT'S THESE BODY PARTS YOU "COOL"	**$600**	WHAT ARE
BORN ARTIS IVEY JR., THIS FATHER OF 6 PICKED UP THE 1995 BEST RAP SOLO PERFORMANCE GRAMMY	**$800**	WHO IS
IT WAS THE REPUBLICANS' 4-WORD SLOGAN IN THE 1924 PRESIDENTIAL CAMPAIGN	**$1000**	WHAT IS

DOUBLE JEOPARDY!

THAT'S COOL

$200	WHAT IS "COOL HAND LUKE"?	**$200**
$400	WHAT IS COOL WHIP?	**$400**
$600	WHAT ARE YOUR HEELS?	**$600**
$800	WHO IS COOLIO?	**$800**
$1000	WHAT IS "KEEP COOL WITH COOLIDGE"?	**$1000**

DOUBLE JEOPARDY!

JOHN CUSACK MOVIES

NICOLAS CAGE & JOHN CUSACK TEAM UP WHEN INMATES HIJACK A PLANE IN THIS 1997 THRILLER	**$200**	WHAT IS
CUSACK WAS THE VOICE OF DIMITRI IN THIS 1997 ANIMATED FILM ABOUT A RUSSIAN PRINCESS	**$400**	WHAT IS
IN AN OFFBEAT 1999 FILM, PUPPETEER CUSACK DISCOVERS A PORTAL INTO THIS FAMOUS ACTOR'S BRAIN	**$600**	WHO IS
CUSACK WAS THIRD BASEMAN BUCK WEAVER IN THIS 1988 FILM ABOUT THE BLACK SOX	**$800**	WHAT IS
CUSACK STARRED WITH MINNIE DRIVER IN THIS 1997 MOVIE ABOUT A MICHIGAN HIGH SCHOOL REUNION	**$1000**	WHAT IS

DOUBLE JEOPARDY!

JOHN CUSACK MOVIES

$200 — WHAT IS "CON AIR"? — $200

$400 — WHAT IS "ANASTASIA"? — $400

$600 — WHO IS JOHN MALKOVICH? — $600

$800 — WHAT IS "EIGHT MEN OUT"? — $800

$1000 — WHAT IS "GROSSE POINTE BLANK"? — $1000

DOUBLE JEOPARDY!

CRUSTACEANS

Clue	Value	Response
BIG ONES (WHICH IS KIND OF AN OXYMORON) ARE CALLED PRAWNS	**$200**	WHAT ARE
WATCH OUT FOR THE GOOSE TYPE OF THESE; THEY MAY GROW ATTACHED TO THE HULL OF YOUR SHIP	**$400**	WHAT ARE
THE DUNGENESS TYPE OF THIS CRUSTACEAN HAS THE SCIENTIFIC NAME CANCER MAGISTER	**$600**	WHAT IS
CRUSTACEAN THAT'S THE TITLE OF A 1979 B-52'S SONG	**$800**	WHAT IS
BLUE WHALES EAT TONS OF THESE TINY CRUSTACEANS WHOSE NAME IS FROM THE NORWEGIAN FOR A FISH'S YOUNG	**$1000**	WHAT ARE

DOUBLE JEOPARDY!

CRUSTACEANS

$200	WHAT ARE SHRIMP?
$400	WHAT ARE BARNACLES? (ACCEPT: CIRRIPEDS)
$600	WHAT IS A CRAB?
$800	WHAT IS A ROCK LOBSTER?
$1000	WHAT ARE KRILL?

DOUBLE JEOPARDY!

ST. LOUIS

FAMILIAR SHAPE OF THE JEFFERSON NATIONAL EXPANSION MEMORIAL'S "GATEWAY"	**$200**	WHAT IS
THIS RAGTIME COMPOSER'S HOME AT 2658A DELMAR BLVD. HAS BEEN RESTORED & OPENED FOR TOURS	**$400**	WHO IS
FOR ALMOST 30 YEARS THIS CHEVY SPORTS CAR, INCLUDING THE STING RAY, WAS BUILT IN ST. LOUIS	**$600**	WHAT IS
THIS COMPANY'S FAMOUS CHECKER-BOARD SQUARE IS IN ST. LOUIS	**$800**	WHAT IS
THIS ST. LOUIS UNIVERSITY FOUNDED IN 1853 HAS A 169-ACRE HILLTOP CAMPUS	**$1000**	WHAT IS

DOUBLE JEOPARDY!

ST. LOUIS

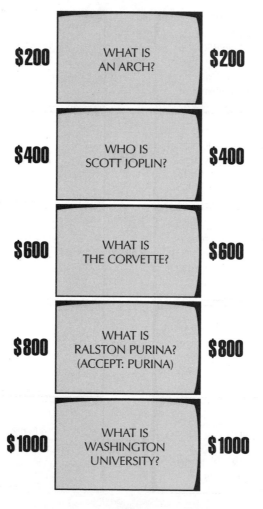

$200 — WHAT IS AN ARCH? — $200

$400 — WHO IS SCOTT JOPLIN? — $400

$600 — WHAT IS THE CORVETTE? — $600

$800 — WHAT IS RALSTON PURINA? (ACCEPT: PURINA) — $800

$1000 — WHAT IS WASHINGTON UNIVERSITY? — $1000

48

DOUBLE JEOPARDY!

BEFORE & AFTER

1961 INVASION OF CUBA WRAPPED IN A TASTY PASTRY	**$200**	WHAT IS
THE LEAD SINGER OF HOLE APPEARING ON CHUCK WOOLERY'S OLD DATING SHOW	**$400**	WHO IS
LONG DISPUTED ISRAELI-PALESTINIAN LAND AREA THAT'S A MINI-SHOPPING COMPLEX	**$600**	WHAT IS
KING KONG PLUNGES FROM EDWARD GIBBON'S MASSIVE HISTORY	**$800**	WHAT IS
JIMMY CARTER'S "ACHY BREAKY" SECRETARY OF STATE	**$1000**	WHO IS

DOUBLE JEOPARDY!

BEFORE & AFTER

$200 — WHAT IS BAY OF PIGS IN A BLANKET? — **$200**

$400 — WHO IS COURTNEY LOVE CONNECTION? — **$400**

$600 — WHAT IS THE GAZA STRIP MALL? — **$600**

$800 — WHAT IS THE DECLINE & FALL OF THE ROMAN EMPIRE STATE BLDG.? — **$800**

$1000 — WHO IS BILLY RAY CYRUS VANCE? — **$1000**

FINAL JEOPARDY!

FAMOUS AMERICAN FAMILIES

IN HARTFORD OVER 200
MANHOLE COVERS MADE
FROM CONFISCATED GUNS
ARE ENGRAVED WITH THE
MOTTO OF THIS LOCAL
FAMILY

WHO ARE

FINAL JEOPARDY!

FAMOUS AMERICAN FAMILIES

WHO ARE THE COLTS?

JEOPARDY!

THE WHITE HOUSE

IT'S THE WHITE HOUSE'S STREET ADDRESS	**$100**	WHAT IS
IT'S THE SHAPE OF THE BLUE ROOM AS WELL AS OF A FAMOUS OFFICE	**$200**	WHAT IS
THE EMANCIPATION PROCLAMATION WAS SIGNED IN THIS FAMOUS ROOM; MAYBE YOU'VE SLEPT THERE	**$300**	WHAT IS
THE WHITE HOUSE WASN'T YET FINISHED IN 1800 WHEN THIS PRESIDENT MOVED IN	**$400**	WHO IS
THIS PRESIDENT HUNG A LARGE MOOSE HEAD IN THE STATE DINING ROOM; A BULL MOOSE, WE PRESUME	**$500**	WHO IS

JEOPARDY!™

THE WHITE HOUSE

$100	WHAT IS 1600 PENNSYLVANIA AVENUE?	$100
$200	WHAT IS OVAL?	$200
$300	WHAT IS THE LINCOLN BEDROOM? (ACCEPT: LINCOLN ROOM)	$300
$400	WHO IS JOHN ADAMS?	$400
$500	WHO IS THEODORE ROOSEVELT?	$500

JEOPARDY!™

UNMENTIONABLES

ANTONIO SABATO JR. WORE THIS DESIGNER'S BLACK BIKINI BRIEFS ON A 90-FOOT BILLBOARD IN TIMES SQUARE	**$100**	WHO IS
ITS TRADEMARK IS COMPOSED OF AN APPLE, GRAPES, GOOSEBERRIES & A CLUSTER OF LEAVES	**$200**	WHAT IS
TYRA BANKS & CLAUDIA SCHIFFER HAVE GRACED THE COVER OF THIS COLUMBUS, OHIO-BASED LINGERIE CATALOG	**$300**	WHAT IS
MADONNA'S BUSTIER WAS STOLEN FROM THIS HOLLYWOOD STORE'S LINGERIE MUSEUM DURING THE 1992 L.A. RIOTS	**$400**	WHAT IS
BVD MADE THIS ONE-PIECE, LONG-SLEEVED UNDERGAR-MENT; YOU NEEDN'T BE A TEAMSTER TO WEAR IT	**$500**	WHAT IS

JEOPARDY!™

UNMENTIONABLES

$100   WHO IS CALVIN KLEIN? $100

$200   WHAT IS FRUIT OF THE LOOM? $200

$300   WHAT IS VICTORIA'S SECRET? $300

$400   WHAT IS FREDERICK'S OF HOLLYWOOD? $400

$500   WHAT IS A UNION SUIT? $500

JEOPARDY!

VERSE

3-LETTER WORD THAT ENDS ERNEST THAYER'S POEM "CASEY AT THE BAT"	**$100**	WHAT IS
HE WROTE, "I HEAR AMERICA SINGING, THE VARIED CAROLS I HEAR"	**$200**	WHO IS
IN "EVERYTHING IN ITS PLACE", ARTHUR GUITERMAN WROTE, "THE BIRDS ARE IN THE BUSHES AND" THIS "IS AT THE DOOR"	**$300**	WHAT IS
HE'S THE REGIMENTAL BHISTI, OR WATER CARRIER, THAT RUDYARD KIPLING MADE FAMOUS	**$400**	WHO IS
IN A ROBERT FROST POEM, A NEIGHBOR INSISTS THESE "MAKE GOOD NEIGHBORS"	**$500**	WHAT ARE

JEOPARDY!™

VERSE

$100 — WHAT IS OUT? — $100

$200 — WHO IS WALT WHITMAN? — $200

$300 — WHAT IS THE WOLF? — $300

$400 — WHO IS GUNGA DIN? — $400

$500 — WHAT ARE GOOD FENCES? — $500

JEOPARDY!™

FAMOUS LATINOS

HIS "VIDA LOCA" HAS INCLUDED TOURS OF DUTY WITH MENUDO & ON "GENERAL HOSPITAL"	**$100**	WHO IS
THE GOLDEN BOY OF THE 1992 OLYMPICS WAS THIS LIGHTWEIGHT BOXER	**$200**	WHO IS
THIS ONETIME "NYPD BLUE" STAR WAS BORN IN BROOKLYN IN 1955	**$300**	WHO IS
HE LED A JULY 26, 1953 ATTACK ON THE MONCADA ARMY BARRACKS IN SANTIAGO DE CUBA	**$400**	WHO IS
REVLON ADDED THIS VOLUPTUOUS "FOOLS RUSH IN" STAR TO ITS STABLE OF MODELS	**$500**	WHO IS

JEOPARDY!™

FAMOUS LATINOS

$100 — WHO IS RICKY MARTIN? — $100

$200 — WHO IS OSCAR DE LA HOYA? — $200

$300 — WHO IS JIMMY SMITS? — $300

$400 — WHO IS FIDEL CASTRO? — $400

$500 — WHO IS SALMA HAYEK? — $500

JEOPARDY!

MUSTY TV

ELIZABETH MONTGOMERY PLAYED QUIRKY COUSIN SERENA AS WELL AS SAMANTHA ON THIS SITCOM	**$100**	WHAT IS
AS PLAYED BY AL LEWIS, GRANDPA ON THIS FAMILY SITCOM COULD TURN INTO A BAT	**$200**	WHAT IS
AN ASSASSIN'S BULLET PARALYZED THIS DETECTIVE PLAYED BY RAYMOND BURR	**$300**	WHO IS
ON TV THIS GERMAN SHEPHERD SERVED AS A PRIVATE IN THE U.S. CAVALRY	**$400**	WHO IS
ABE VIGODA PLAYED THIS DETECTIVE ON "BARNEY MILLER" & A SPIN-OFF	**$500**	WHO IS

JEOPARDY!

MUSTY TV

$100 — WHAT IS "BEWITCHED"? — $100

$200 — WHAT IS "THE MUNSTERS"? — $200

$300 — WHO IS (ROBERT) IRONSIDE? — $300

$400 — WHO IS RIN TIN TIN? (ACCEPT: RINTIE) — $400

$500 — WHO IS (PHIL) FISH? — $500

JEOPARDY!

HOMOPHONES

ANOTHER NAME FOR A BUCKET, OR YOUR COLORING IF ONE FALLS ON YOU	**$100**	WHAT IS
YOU OPEN IT IN A FIREPLACE, OR IT MAY MEAN YOU'RE ALREADY WAY TOO WARM	**$200**	WHAT IS
A CAUSTIC SUBSTANCE IN SOAP, OR AN UNTRUTH	**$300**	WHAT IS
A TYPE OF SANDWICH BREAD, OR TWISTED, LIKE A SENSE OF HUMOR	**$400**	WHAT IS
IT'S A CORRIDOR, OR HOW YOU MIGHT CARRY SOMETHING DOWN ONE	**$500**	WHAT IS

JEOPARDY!

HOMOPHONES

$100   WHAT IS
PAIL/PALE?   **$100**

$200   WHAT IS
FLUE/FLU?   **$200**

$300   WHAT IS
LYE/LIE?   **$300**

$400   WHAT IS
WRY/RYE?   **$400**

$500   WHAT IS
HALL/HAUL?   **$500**

DOUBLE JEOPARDY!

THE COSSACKS ARE COMING!

FOR HIS BOOKS ON THE COSSACKS OF THE DON RIVER, MIKHAIL SHOLOKHOV WON THIS TOP PRIZE IN 1965	**$200**	WHAT IS
WHILE THERE WERE A FEW MECHANIZED UNITS, THE COSSACKS IN WWII MAINLY SERVED IN THESE UNITS	**$400**	WHAT ARE
FOR A WHILE THE CITY OF KHARKIV, FOUNDED AS A COSSACK OUT-POST, REPLACED KIEV AS CAPITAL OF THIS REPUBLIC	**$600**	WHAT IS
IN 1992 THIS RUSSIAN PRESIDENT GRANTED THE COSSACKS THE STATUS OF AN ETHNIC GROUP	**$800**	WHO IS
THE NAME COSSACK COMES FROM "KAZAK", A WORD IN THIS LANGUAGE THAT ALSO GAVE US THE WORD YOGURT	**$1000**	WHAT IS

DOUBLE JEOPARDY!

THE COSSACKS ARE COMING!

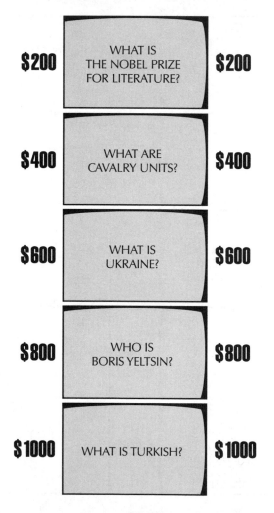

$200
WHAT IS
THE NOBEL PRIZE
FOR LITERATURE?
$200

$400
WHAT ARE
CAVALRY UNITS?
$400

$600
WHAT IS
UKRAINE?
$600

$800
WHO IS
BORIS YELTSIN?
$800

$1000
WHAT IS TURKISH?
$1000

DOUBLE JEOPARDY!

PSYCH 102

THE "WRITER'S" TYPE IS A COMMON FORM OF THIS, A PSYCHO-LOGICAL OBSTACLE TO COMPLETING A PROJECT	**$200**	WHAT IS
BIPOLAR DISORDER IS AN ILLNESS COMMONLY REFERRED TO AS "MANIC" THIS	**$400**	WHAT IS
THIS COGNITIVE PROCESS HAS 3 STAGES: ACQUISITION, RETENTION & RETRIEVAL	**$600**	WHAT IS
IN WWI, "POST-TRAU-MATIC STRESS DISOR-DER" WAS KNOWN AS "COMBAT FATIGUE" OR THIS ALLITERATIVE 2-WORD TERM	**$800**	WHAT IS
2-LETTER FREUDIAN TERM FOR THE DEEP PART OF THE PSYCHE GOVERNED BY THE PLEASURE PRINCIPLE	**$1000**	WHAT IS

DOUBLE JEOPARDY!

PSYCH 102

$200   WHAT IS A BLOCK?   **$200**

$400   WHAT IS DEPRESSION?   **$400**

$600   WHAT IS MEMORY?   **$600**

$800   WHAT IS SHELL SHOCK?   **$800**

$1000   WHAT IS THE ID?   **$1000**

DOUBLE JEOPARDY!

1960s MUSIC

IN 1968 THIS DUO SERENADED MRS. ROBINSON	**$200**	WHO ARE
IN 1963 JIMMY GILMER HIT NO. 1 WITH "SUGAR SHACK"; IN 1969 THIS GROUP HIT NO. 1 WITH "SUGAR SUGAR"	**$400**	WHAT ARE
DUE TO AN OWNERSHIP DISPUTE, THIS 1966 NO. 1 HIT BY THE TROGGS WAS RELEASED SIMULTANEOUSLY ON 2 LABELS	**$600**	WHAT IS
THIS GROUP'S 1965 HIT "DO YOU BELIEVE IN MAGIC" WAS USED IN 1990s TV COMMERCIALS BY McDONALD'S	**$800**	WHO IS
THIS 1963 HIT BY KYU SAKAMOTO WAS RELEASED IN JAPAN AS "UE O MUITE ARUKO", OR "I LOOK UP WHEN I WALK"	**$1000**	WHAT IS

DOUBLE JEOPARDY!

1960s MUSIC

$200	WHO ARE SIMON & GARFUNKEL?	**$200**
$400	WHAT ARE THE ARCHIES?	**$400**
$600	WHAT IS "WILD THING"?	**$600**
$800	WHO IS THE LOVIN' SPOONFUL?	**$800**
$1000	WHAT IS "SUKIYAKI"?	**$1000**

DOUBLE JEOPARDY!

SCOOPS

IN 1936 EDGAR SNOW REACHED SHAANXI PROVINCE & GOT AN INTERVIEW WITH THIS FUTURE CHAIRMAN	**$200**	WHO IS
IN 1945 REPORTER WILLIAM LAURENCE GOT TO FLY OVER THIS CITY FOR THE SECOND A-BOMB DROP	**$400**	WHAT IS
REPORTER ANDREA MITCHELL GOT THE SCOOP THAT GEORGE BUSH HAD MADE THIS CONTROVERSIAL CHOICE AUG. 16, 1988	**$600**	WHAT IS
THE REGISTER OF THIS COUNTY NEAR L.A. WON A 1996 PULITZER FOR REPORTING ON FERTILITY CLINIC FRAUD	**$800**	WHAT IS
AMONG SCOOPS BY THIS "WASHINGTON MERRY-GO-ROUND" COLUM-NIST WERE FACTS LEAD-ING TO THE CENSURE OF SEN. THOMAS DODD	**$1000**	WHO IS

DOUBLE JEOPARDY!

SCOOPS

$200	WHO IS MAO TSE-TUNG?	**$200**
$400	WHAT IS NAGASAKI?	**$400**
$600	WHAT IS DAN QUAYLE (FOR RUNNING MATE)?	**$600**
$800	WHAT IS ORANGE COUNTY?	**$800**
$1000	WHO IS JACK ANDERSON? (ACCEPT: DREW PEARSON)	**$1000**

DOUBLE JEOPARDY!

FARAWAY PLACES

TIMBUKTU IN MALI WAS ONCE A MAJOR CARAVAN CENTER FOR THOSE CROSSING THIS DESERT	**$200**	WHAT IS
THIS REMOTE ASIAN NATION ONCE HAD "OUTER" ATTACHED TO ITS NAME; AN "INNER" REGION BELONGS TO CHINA	**$400**	WHAT IS
TOURS IN THIS FAR-AWAY LAND INCLUDE A SAFARI IN ROYAL CHITWAN NATIONAL PARK & RAFTING TRIPS NEAR KATMANDU	**$600**	WHAT IS
PUNTA ARENAS, IN THIS COUNTRY, IS THE WORLD'S SOUTHERN-MOST CITY ON A CONTINENTAL MAINLAND	**$800**	WHAT IS
A CITY "UZ"ING CULTURE, SAMARKAND IN THIS FORMER SOVIET REPUBLIC IS THE SITE OF TAMERLANE'S TOMB	**$1000**	WHAT IS

DOUBLE JEOPARDY!

FARAWAY PLACES

$200   WHAT IS THE SAHARA? $200

$400   WHAT IS MONGOLIA? $400

$600   WHAT IS NEPAL? $600

$800   WHAT IS CHILE? $800

$1000   WHAT IS UZBEKISTAN? $1000

74

DOUBLE JEOPARDY!

GOING "STRAIGHT"

A POKER HAND CONSISTING OF THE 6, 5, 4, 3 & 2 OF CLUBS	**$200**	WHAT IS
A PIECE OF WOOD OR METAL, LIKE A RULER, THAT CAN BE USED TO DRAW UNWAVERING LINES	**$400**	WHAT IS
GRACIE ALLEN WAS MARRIED TO HERS	**$600**	WHAT IS
1999 DAVID LYNCH FILM ABOUT AN ELDERLY MAN'S TRIP TO VISIT HIS BROTHER	**$800**	WHAT IS
IN POLITICAL LINGO, TO "VOTE" THIS IS TO SUBMIT A BALLOT SUPPORTING CANDIDATES OF JUST ONE PARTY	**$1000**	WHAT IS

DOUBLE JEOPARDY!

GOING "STRAIGHT"

$200	WHAT IS A STRAIGHT FLUSH?	$200
$400	WHAT IS A STRAIGHTEDGE?	$400
$600	WHAT IS A STRAIGHT MAN?	$600
$800	WHAT IS "THE STRAIGHT STORY"?	$800
$1000	WHAT IS THE STRAIGHT TICKET?	$1000

FINAL JEOPARDY!

STATE CAPITALS

IN 1765 THIS CITY WAS
NAMED IN HONOR OF THE
PEACEFUL RESOLUTION OF
A BOUNDARY DISPUTE

WHAT IS

FINAL JEOPARDY!

STATE CAPITALS

WHAT IS CONCORD
(NEW HAMPSHIRE)?

JEOPARDY!

MARCH OF TIME

ONCE HOME TO AL CAPONE & A BIRDMAN, IT CLOSED ITS CELL DOORS MARCH 21, 1963	**$100**	WHAT IS
ON MARCH 25, 1957 6 COUNTRIES SIGNED THE TREATY OF ROME TO FORM THIS, THE EEC	**$200**	WHAT IS
ON MARCH 8, 1999 SCIENTIST WEN HO LEE WAS FIRED FROM THIS NEW MEXICO NATIONAL LABORATORY	**$300**	WHAT IS
THE U.S. VOTED AGAINST JOINING THIS ORGANIZATION MARCH 19, 1920; TODAY WE'RE HERE & IT ISN'T	**$400**	WHAT IS
ON MARCH 1, 1954 THE U.S. CONDUCTED THE FIRST OF A SERIES OF HYDROGEN BOMB TESTS ON THIS PACIFIC ATOLL	**$500**	WHAT IS

JEOPARDY!

MARCH OF TIME

$100	WHAT IS ALCATRAZ?	$100
$200	WHAT IS THE EUROPEAN ECONOMIC COMMUNITY?	$200
$300	WHAT IS LOS ALAMOS?	$300
$400	WHAT IS THE LEAGUE OF NATIONS?	$400
$500	WHAT IS BIKINI ATOLL?	$500

JEOPARDY!

BLACK AMERICANS

IN 1989, AT AGE 52, HE BECAME THE YOUNGEST MAN EVER TO SERVE AS CHAIRMAN OF THE JOINT CHIEFS OF STAFF	**$100**	WHO IS
THIS MONTGOMERY SEAMSTRESS WAS THROWN OFF A BUS ONE OTHER TIME BEFORE HER FAMOUS DEC. 1, 1955 INCIDENT	**$200**	WHO IS
THIS KILLER COMIC HAS SHOWN HE CAN "BRING THE PAIN" & BE PART OF THE "LETHAL WEAPON" FRANCHISE	**$300**	WHO IS
THIS AUTHOR OF "I KNOW WHY THE CAGED BIRD SINGS" WON THE NAACP'S SPINGARN MEDAL IN 1994	**$400**	WHO IS
ONCE WHITE HOUSE DIRECTOR OF PUBLIC LIAISON, SHE BECAME THE USA'S FIRST BLACK SECRETARY OF LABOR IN 1997	**$500**	WHO IS

JEOPARDY!™

BLACK AMERICANS

$100 WHO IS COLIN POWELL? **$100**

$200 WHO IS ROSA PARKS? **$200**

$300 WHO IS CHRIS ROCK? **$300**

$400 WHO IS MAYA ANGELOU? **$400**

$500 WHO IS ALEXIS HERMAN? **$500**

JEOPARDY!™

ASSOCIATES

Clue	Value	Response
AN ASSOCIATE OF EQUAL RANK; YOU MAY BE A "JOLLY GOOD" ONE	$100	WHAT IS
IT CAN REFER TO AN INTIMATE FRIEND OR TO A COMMUNIST	$200	WHAT IS
THE FAMILIAL NAME FOR A CO-MEMBER OF A MEN'S GREEK LETTER ASSOCIATION	$300	WHAT IS
FROM A WORD FOR "TO LABOR TOGETHER", IT'S ONE WHO HELPS THE ENEMY FORCE OCCUPYING HIS COUNTRY	$400	WHAT IS
PERHAPS FROM THE GREEK FOR "TIME", IT'S A LONGTIME "OLD" PAL	$500	WHAT IS

JEOPARDY!

ASSOCIATES

$100   WHAT IS A FELLOW? $100

$200   WHAT IS COMRADE? $200

$300   WHAT IS A FRAT(ERNITY) BROTHER? $300

$400   WHAT IS A COLLABORATOR? $400

$500   WHAT IS A CRONY? $500

JEOPARDY!

HISTORIC NAMES

ONE OF THE SIGNERS OF ISRAEL'S DECLARATION OF INDEPENDENCE, SHE BECAME PRIME MINISTER IN 1969	**$100**	WHO IS
BEFORE DESIGNING THE FIRST SUCCESSFUL STEAMBOAT, HE WORKED AS A PORTRAIT PAINTER	**$200**	WHO IS
THIS "NINE DAYS' QUEEN" OF ENGLAND WAS A GRAND-DAUGHTER OF HENRY VIII's SISTER MARY	**$300**	WHO IS
THIS REDSHIRTS LEADER LED HIS FINAL CAMPAIGN WHEN HE FOUGHT FOR FRANCE IN THE FRANCO-PRUSSIAN WAR	**$400**	WHO IS
A SIOUX LEADER AT THE TIME OF THE LITTLE BIGHORN, HIS INDIAN NAME WAS TATANKA YOTANKA	**$500**	WHO IS

JEOPARDY!

HISTORIC NAMES

$100   WHO IS GOLDA MEIR?   **$100**

$200   WHO IS ROBERT FULTON?   **$200**

$300   WHO IS (LADY) JANE GREY?   **$300**

$400   WHO IS GIUSEPPE GARIBALDI?   **$400**

$500   WHO IS SITTING BULL?   **$500**

JEOPARDY!

EUROPEAN VACATION

Clue	Value	Response
ACCORDING TO THE MOVIES, THIS LANDMARK IS VISIBLE FROM EVERY WINDOW IN EVERY BUILDING IN PARIS	**$100**	WHAT IS
IN THIS CZECH CAPITAL, YOU CAN VISIT A HOME WHERE MOZART COMPOSED PART OF "DON GIOVANNI"	**$200**	WHAT IS
WHILE IN ROME, IT'S POSSIBLE TO STAND WITH ONE FOOT IN EACH OF THESE COUNTRIES	**$300**	WHAT ARE
TO SEE HIS "NIGHT WATCH", HEAD TO THE RIJKSMUSEUM IN AMSTERDAM	**$400**	WHO IS
WHILE MOM'S AT CHRISTIANSBORG PALACE IN THIS CITY, DAD MAY HEAD DOWN THE STREET TO THE EROTIC MUSEUM	**$500**	WHAT IS

JEOPARDY!

EUROPEAN VACATION

$100	WHAT IS THE EIFFEL TOWER?	**$100**
$200	WHAT IS PRAGUE?	**$200**
$300	WHAT ARE ITALY & VATICAN CITY?	**$300**
$400	WHO IS REMBRANDT (VAN RIJN)?	**$400**
$500	WHAT IS COPENHAGEN?	**$500**

JEOPARDY!

NOW THAT'S COMEDY

IN "TAKE THE MONEY AND RUN", THIS COMEDIAN BUNGLES A BANK ROBBERY BECAUSE NO ONE CAN READ HIS NOTE	**$100**	WHO IS
ONE OF THESE DAVID LETTERMAN BITS IS "LEAST POPULAR CANDY BARS"; NO. 4 IS "GOOD 'N' LINTY"	**$200**	WHAT ARE
IN AN EARLY ROUTINE, BOB NEWHART INSTRUCTS DRIVERS OF THESE ON PULLING AWAY JUST AS PEOPLE REACH THE DOORS	**$300**	WHAT ARE
BUXOM WOMEN LOSING THEIR CLOTHES WAS A STAPLE OF THIS COMIC'S SHOW, ON BRITISH TV UNTIL 1989	**$400**	WHO IS
DANNY THOMAS WAS A MASTER OF THIS "TAKE" IN WHICH HE'D GET STARTLING NEWS WHILE EATING OR DRINKING	**$500**	WHAT IS

JEOPARDY!™

NOW THAT'S COMEDY

$100 WHO IS WOODY ALLEN? **$100**

$200 WHAT ARE TOP TEN LISTS? **$200**

$300 WHAT ARE BUSES? **$300**

$400 WHO IS BENNY HILL? **$400**

$500 WHAT IS A SPIT TAKE? **$500**

DOUBLE JEOPARDY!

CANADIAN STUFF, EH?

THIS "STAMPEDE" CITY LIES IN THE FOOTHILLS OF THE CANADIAN ROCKIES, SO IT'S NICKNAMED THE "FOOTHILLS CITY"	**$200**	WHAT IS
PIE-IX, DE L'EGLISE & L'ASSOMPTION ARE STOPS ON THIS CITY'S METRO	**$400**	WHAT IS
IT'S BEEN CALLED "BRITAIN'S OLDEST COLONY", BUT IT'S CANADA'S "NEW"EST PROVINCE	**$600**	WHAT IS
LADY SLIPPER DRIVE, A SCENIC ROUTE IN THIS TINY ISLAND PROVINCE, IS NAMED FOR THE PROVINCE'S OFFICIAL FLOWER	**$800**	WHAT IS
2 OF THESE LONG-TUSKED WHALES ADORN THE COAT OF ARMS OF CANADA'S NORTHWEST TERRITORIES	**$1000**	WHAT ARE

DOUBLE JEOPARDY!

CANADIAN STUFF, EH?

$200 WHAT IS CALGARY? **$200**

$400 WHAT IS MONTREAL? **$400**

$600 WHAT IS NEWFOUNDLAND? **$600**

$800 WHAT IS PRINCE EDWARD ISLAND? (ACCEPT: P.E.I.) **$800**

$1000 WHAT ARE NARWHALS? **$1000**

DOUBLE JEOPARDY!

BEAUTY

SHORT MASCULINE NICKNAME THAT'S ALSO A WOMEN'S SHORT HAIRSTYLE	**$200**	WHAT IS
COSMETIC WHOSE NAME IS SPANISH FOR "MASK"	**$400**	WHAT IS
"BECAUSE I'M WORTH IT" IS A CLASSIC SLOGAN OF THIS LINE OF COSMETICS FROM PARIS	**$600**	WHAT IS
A COSMETIC USED AS A BASE FOR MAKEUP; PERHAPS THE FORD MODELING AGENCY HAS ITS OWN BRAND	**$800**	WHAT IS
FROM LATIN FOR "TO SOFTEN", THIS WORD IS FOUND IN MANY SKIN CARE PRODUCT ADS	**$1000**	WHAT IS

DOUBLE JEOPARDY!™

BEAUTY

$200	WHAT IS BOB?	**$200**
$400	WHAT IS MASCARA?	**$400**
$600	WHAT IS L'OREAL?	**$600**
$800	WHAT IS FOUNDATION?	**$800**
$1000	WHAT IS EMOLLIENT?	**$1000**

DOUBLE JEOPARDY!

SPORTS

AFTER 36 SEASONS IN THIS STADIUM NAMED FOR A U.S. SENATOR, THE REDSKINS MOVED TO A NEW FACILITY IN 1997	**$200**	WHAT IS
THIS COACH OF THE NBA'S LAKERS, KNICKS & HEAT IS AUTHOR OF A BOOK CALLED "THE WINNER WITHIN"	**$400**	WHO IS
IN 1996, WITH THE OAKLAND A'S, THIS FIRST BASEMAN HIT 52 HOME RUNS—HE WAS JUST WARMING UP	**$600**	WHO IS
HE WAS THE INDY 500 ROOKIE OF THE YEAR IN 1965; HIS SON MICHAEL GOT THE HONOR IN 1984	**$800**	WHO IS
ABE MITCHELL IS THE GOLFER DEPICTED ON THIS CUP SOUGHT BY TEAMS FROM THE U.S. & EUROPE	**$1000**	WHAT IS

DOUBLE JEOPARDY!

SPORTS

$200	WHAT IS RFK STADIUM?	**$200**
$400	WHO IS PAT RILEY?	**$400**
$600	WHO IS MARK McGWIRE?	**$600**
$800	WHO IS MARIO ANDRETTI?	**$800**
$1000	WHAT IS THE RYDER CUP?	**$1000**

DOUBLE JEOPARDY!

MIDDLE NAMES

MIDDLE NAME OF BASEBALL PITCHER LYNN RYAN JR.	**$200**	WHAT IS
MIDDLE NAME OF SONGWRITER JAMES McCARTNEY	**$400**	WHAT IS
MIDDLE NAME OF DIRECTOR ERNST BERGMAN	**$600**	WHAT IS
MIDDLE NAME OF CIVIL RIGHTS LEADER LEROY CLEAVER	**$800**	WHAT IS
MIDDLE NAME OF COMMUNICATION THEORIST HERBERT McLUHAN	**$1000**	WHAT IS

DOUBLE JEOPARDY!

MIDDLE NAMES

$200 — WHAT IS NOLAN? — $200

$400 — WHAT IS PAUL? — $400

$600 — WHAT IS INGMAR? — $600

$800 — WHAT IS ELDRIDGE? — $800

$1000 — WHAT IS MARSHALL? — $1000

DOUBLE JEOPARDY!

LOUIS XIV

LOUIS' NICKNAME; HE USED THE SYMBOL AS HIS EMBLEM	**$200**	WHAT IS
CHARLES DE BATZ, SÍEUR D'ARTAGNAN, A SOLDIER IN LOUIS' SERVICE, IS WELL KNOWN BECAUSE OF THIS 1844 NOVEL	**$400**	WHAT IS
IT WAS LOUIS' MONEY PIT; ONCE HE STARTED BUILDING THIS ROYAL RESIDENCE IN THE 1660s IT WAS HARD TO STOP	**$600**	WHAT IS
AT THIS AGE LOUIS SAID, "TODAY I AM A MAN" & DUMPED HIS MOTHER AS REGENT	**$800**	WHAT IS
WANTING THE HUGUENOTS TO CONVERT, LOUIS REVOKED THE EDICT OF THIS IN 1685	**$1000**	WHAT IS

DOUBLE JEOPARDY!

LOUIS XIV

$200   WHAT IS THE SUN KING?   **$200**

$400   WHAT IS "THE THREE MUSKETEERS"?   **$400**

$600   WHAT IS THE PALACE OF VERSAILLES?   **$600**

$800   WHAT IS 13?   **$800**

$1000   WHAT IS NANTES?   **$1000**

DOUBLE JEOPARDY!

STARTS & ENDS WITH "T"

IF YOU NEVER SAY DYE, SAY THIS, A LIGHT DYE FOR THE HAIR	**$200**	WHAT IS
DINING ACCESSORY USED TO PROTECT THE TABLE FROM A HOT DISH	**$400**	WHAT IS
ONE TO SEE THE MOVIE "SPEED" IS GOOD; ONE FOR SPEEDING IS BAD	**$600**	WHAT IS
THIS PROFESSIONAL WILL STUFF YOUR TURKEY...OR YOUR MOOSE, OR YOUR MARLIN	**$800**	WHAT IS
IT'S AN EXTENDED OUTLINE OF A MOVIE	**$1000**	WHAT IS

DOUBLE JEOPARDY!

STARTS & ENDS WITH "T"

$200 — WHAT IS TINT? — **$200**

$400 — WHAT IS A TRIVET? — **$400**

$600 — WHAT IS A TICKET? — **$600**

$800 — WHAT IS A TAXIDERMIST? — **$800**

$1000 — WHAT IS A TREATMENT? — **$1000**

FINAL JEOPARDY!

1990s MEDICINE

IN 1998 AN ASPIRIN-
ACETOMINOPHEN-
CAFFEINE PILL BECAME THE
FIRST FDA-APPROVED
OVER-THE-COUNTER PILL
FOR THIS

WHAT IS

1990s MEDICINE

WHAT IS MIGRAINE?
(ACCEPT: MIGRAINE
HEADACHES)

JEOPARDY!

LITERARY EPICS

THIS POET CAST HIMSELF AS THE PROTAGONIST OF THE "DIVINE COMEDY"	**$100**	WHO IS
THIS TENNYSON WORK BASED ON LEGENDS OF KING ARTHUR FILLS 12 BOOKS	**$200**	WHAT ARE
PART OF THE ACTION OF THIS OLD ENGLISH POEM TAKES PLACE IN HROTHGAR'S GREAT HALL, HEOROT	**$300**	WHAT IS
THE "ARGONAUTICA" BY APOLLONIUS OF RHODES TELLS THE STORY OF THE QUEST FOR THIS OBJECT	**$400**	WHAT IS
THIS ANCIENT MESOPOTAMIAN KING IS THE HERO OF THE EARLIEST KNOWN EPIC POEM	**$500**	WHO IS

JEOPARDY!™

LITERARY EPICS

$100	WHO IS DANTE (ALIGHIERI)?	**$100**
$200	WHAT ARE "IDYLLS OF THE KING"?	**$200**
$300	WHAT IS "BEOWULF"?	**$300**
$400	WHAT IS THE GOLDEN FLEECE?	**$400**
$500	WHO IS GILGAMESH?	**$500**

JEOPARDY!™

BIG IN JAPAN

BEAUTY IN THIS BODY PART IS SO VALUED THAT A COMMON INSULT IS "YOUR MOTHER HAS AN OUTIE"	**$100**	WHAT IS
THE FILM "A RIVER RUNS THROUGH IT" INSPIRED A JAPANESE CRAZE FOR THIS SPORT	**$200**	WHAT IS
THIS TOKYO TRANSIT SYSTEM IS SO POPULAR, "PLATFORM PUSHERS" MAKE SURE EVERYONE GETS ON	**$300**	WHAT IS
THE WWII DIARY OF THIS DUTCH JEWISH TEENAGER IS WIDELY READ BY YOUNG JAPANESE GIRLS	**$400**	WHO IS
THIS GROUP THAT RECORDED SONGS LIKE "SURRENDER" & "I WANT YOU TO WANT ME" LIVE IN JAPAN REMAINS POPULAR THERE	**$500**	WHAT IS

JEOPARDY!

BIG IN JAPAN

$100 — WHAT IS THE NAVEL? (ACCEPT: BELLY BUTTON) — **$100**

$200 — WHAT IS (FLY) FISHING? (ACCEPT: BASS FISHING) — **$200**

$300 — WHAT IS THE SUBWAY? — **$300**

$400 — WHO IS ANNE FRANK? — **$400**

$500 — WHAT IS CHEAP TRICK? — **$500**

JEOPARDY!

TELEVISION

THE APARTMENT COMPLEX LOCATED AT 4616 ON THIS TITLE L.A. STREET WAS HOME TO SOME "FOX"Y LADIES	**$100**	WHAT IS
"PROMISED LAND" WITH GERALD McRANEY WAS SPUN OFF FROM THIS HEAVENLY CBS SERIES	**$200**	WHAT IS
HE'S PLAYED PETE RYAN, ALEXANDER MUNDY & JONATHAN HART	**$300**	WHO IS
MANDY PATINKIN LEFT, THEN RETURNED TO THE ROLE OF DR. GEIGER ON THIS DRAMA	**$400**	WHAT IS
SHE'S BEEN HALF OF "CAGNEY & LACEY" & THE MOTHER OF "JUDGING AMY"	**$500**	WHO IS

JEOPARDY!

TELEVISION

$100	WHAT IS "MELROSE PLACE"?	**$100**
$200	WHAT IS "TOUCHED BY AN ANGEL"?	**$200**
$300	WHO IS ROBERT WAGNER?	**$300**
$400	WHAT IS "CHICAGO HOPE"?	**$400**
$500	WHO IS TYNE DALY?	**$500**

JEOPARDY!

ANIMALS

Clue	Value	Response
THE MONKEY-EATING SPECIES OF THIS BIRD LIVES IN THE PHILIPPINES; THE BALD SPECIES LIVES IN THE U.S.	**$100**	WHAT IS
THIS "RIVER HORSE" CAN WEIGH MORE THAN 8,000 POUNDS	**$200**	WHAT IS
THE ICHNEUMON IS AN AFRICAN SPECIES OF THIS ANIMAL FAMED FOR ITS SNAKE-FIGHTING ABILITIES	**$300**	WHAT IS
THESE BIRDS RANGE IN SIZE FROM THE 1-FOOT BLUE TO THE 4-FOOT EMPEROR	**$400**	WHAT ARE
THESE LIZARDS THAT INCLUDE THE KOMODO DRAGON WOULD BE EFFECTIVE AT PATROLLING THE HALL	**$500**	WHAT ARE

JEOPARDY!

ANIMALS

$100	WHAT IS THE EAGLE?	**$100**
$200	WHAT IS THE HIPPOPOTAMUS?	**$200**
$300	WHAT IS THE MONGOOSE?	**$300**
$400	WHAT ARE PENGUINS?	**$400**
$500	WHAT ARE MONITOR LIZARDS?	**$500**

JEOPARDY!™

SPENCERS FOR HIRE

Clue	Value	Response
SPENCER WAS THE MIDDLE NAME OF THIS "LITTLE TRAMP"	$100	WHO IS
AS SECRETARY OF THIS D.C. INSTITUTION, SPENCER BAIRD BEGAN THE COLLECTION HOUSED IN ITS MUSEUMS	$200	WHAT IS
THIS ACTOR WHO PLAYED FATHER FLANAGAN IN 1938 ONCE ASPIRED TO THE PRIESTHOOD	$300	WHO IS
19th CENTURY DARWINIAN THINKER HERBERT SPENCER IS CREDITED WITH COINING THE PHRASE "SURVIVAL OF" THESE	$400	WHO ARE
"GIMME SOME LOVIN'" & "I'M A MAN" WERE HITS FOR THIS MAN'S "GROUP"	$500	WHO IS

JEOPARDY!™

SPENCERS FOR HIRE

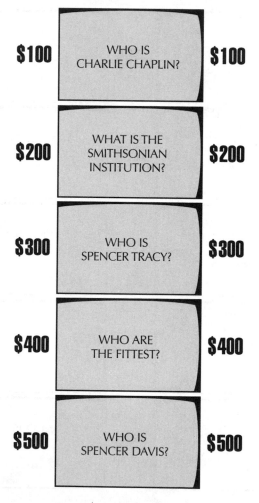

$100 — WHO IS CHARLIE CHAPLIN? — $100

$200 — WHAT IS THE SMITHSONIAN INSTITUTION? — $200

$300 — WHO IS SPENCER TRACY? — $300

$400 — WHO ARE THE FITTEST? — $400

$500 — WHO IS SPENCER DAVIS? — $500

JEOPARDY!

"C" OF LOVE

Clue	Value	Response
THE TITLE OF A 1958 CONNIE FRANCIS SONG CALLS THIS LOVE GOD "STUPID"	$100	WHO IS
IF YOU DIDN'T SHOW UP FOR A BLIND DATE, YOU HAVE THESE KIND OF "FEET"	$200	WHAT ARE
FROM AN OLD WORD FOR "CAPE", IT'S AN OLDER PERSON WHO, FOR PROPRIETY'S SAKE, ACCOMPANIES YOUNG UNMARRIEDS	$300	WHAT IS
THE YOUNGEST DAUGHTER OF KING LEAR, SHE WAS THE ONLY ONE WHO REALLY LOVED HIM	$400	WHO IS
ITALIAN FOR "WITH LOVE", IT'S THE MUSICAL DIRECTION TO PLAY OR SING LOVINGLY	$500	WHAT IS

JEOPARDY!™

"C" OF LOVE

$100	WHO IS CUPID?	**$100**
$200	WHAT ARE COLD FEET?	**$200**
$300	WHAT IS A CHAPERONE?	**$300**
$400	WHO IS CORDELIA?	**$400**
$500	WHAT IS CON AMORE?	**$500**

DOUBLE JEOPARDY!

AMERICAN HISTORY

Clue	Value	Response
BRITISH COMMANDER SIR EDWARD PAKENHAM DIED IN THE BATTLE OF THIS CITY, FOUGHT AFTER A TREATY ENDED THE WAR OF 1812	**$200**	WHAT IS
ON MARCH 27, 1964, THIS LARGEST ALASKA CITY WAS HIT BY AN 8.4 EARTHQUAKE	**$400**	WHAT IS
IN 1787 ARTHUR ST. CLAIR BECAME THE FIRST GOVERNOR OF THIS VAST "TERRITORY" NORTH OF THE OHIO RIVER	**$600**	WHAT IS
ON NOVEMBER 14, 1889, THE NEW YORK WORLD CALLED THIS JOURNALIST'S TRIP "THE LONGEST JOURNEY KNOWN TO MANKIND"	**$800**	WHO IS
THIS TRAIL THAT TOOK TEXAS CATTLE TO KANSAS WAS NAMED FOR A TRADER NAMED JESSE	**$1000**	WHAT IS

DOUBLE JEOPARDY!™

AMERICAN HISTORY

$200	WHAT IS NEW ORLEANS?	**$200**
$400	WHAT IS ANCHORAGE?	**$400**
$600	WHAT IS THE NORTHWEST TERRITORY?	**$600**
$800	WHO IS NELLIE BLY? (ACCEPT: ELIZABETH COCHRANE SEAMAN)	**$800**
$1000	WHAT IS THE CHISHOLM TRAIL?	**$1000**

DOUBLE JEOPARDY!

DOCS

Clue	Value	Response
ALBERT SABIN, BEST KNOWN FOR HIS ORAL VACCINE FOR THIS, ALSO DEVELOPED A VACCINE FOR DENGUE FEVER	**$200**	WHAT IS
IN 1967 THIS "BABY AND CHILD CARE" AUTHOR RESIGNED AS A COLLEGE TEACHER TO JOIN THE ANTIWAR MOVEMENT FULL-TIME	**$400**	WHO IS
MANY AMERICANS CAN GIVE THEIR HEARTFELT THANKS TO THIS HOUSTON SURGEON, THE FIRST TO REPAIR AN ANEURYSM	**$600**	WHO IS
HANS SELYE PIONEERED THE STUDY OF THIS & WROTE A BOOK ABOUT IT "WITHOUT DISTRESS"	**$800**	WHAT IS
IN 1778 THIS SMALLPOX VACCINE DEVELOPER WROTE A PAPER ON THE MURDEROUS HABITS OF THE YOUNG CUCKOO BIRD	**$1000**	WHO IS

DOUBLE JEOPARDY!

DOCS

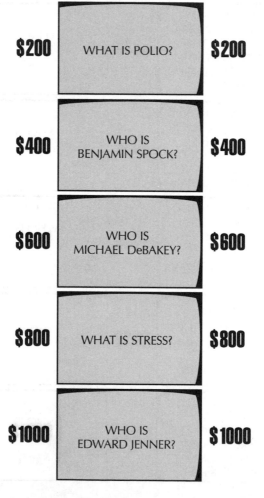

$200   WHAT IS POLIO? $200

$400   WHO IS
        BENJAMIN SPOCK? $400

$600   WHO IS
        MICHAEL DeBAKEY? $600

$800   WHAT IS STRESS? $800

$1000   WHO IS
        EDWARD JENNER? $1000

DOUBLE JEOPARDY!

WE, THE JURY

IN 1970 THE SUPREME COURT DECLARED THIS STANDARD NUMBER OF JURORS A "HISTORICAL ACCIDENT"	**$200**	WHAT IS
WHAT A JURY DOES WHEN IT CAN'T AGREE, OR WHAT IT MAY SENTENCE A MURDERER TO	**$400**	WHAT IS
IN A PERSONAL INJURY LAWSUIT, THE JURY MAY CALCULATE BOTH PUNITIVE & COMPENSATORY TYPES OF THESE	**$600**	WHAT ARE
THE RIGHT TO HAVE A JURY OF THESE, MEANING ONE'S EQUALS, NOT LORDS, IS MENTIONED IN THE MAGNA CARTA	**$800**	WHAT ARE
A LAWYER'S REJECTION OF A PROSPECTIVE JUROR, IT MAY BE "FOR CAUSE" OR "PEREMPTORY"	**$1000**	WHAT IS

DOUBLE JEOPARDY!

WE, THE JURY

$200	WHAT IS 12?	**$200**
$400	WHAT IS HANG?	**$400**
$600	WHAT ARE DAMAGES?	**$600**
$800	WHAT ARE (ONE'S) PEERS?	**$800**
$1000	WHAT IS A CHALLENGE?	**$1000**

DOUBLE JEOPARDY!

FILMS OF THE '70s

WARNER BROS. HAD RIGHTS TO "THE TOWER", FOX HAD RIGHTS TO "THE GLASS INFERNO" & THIS MOVIE WAS THE RESULT	**$200**	WHAT IS
14-LETTER WORD COINED TO DESCRIBE FILMS LIKE "SHAFT" & "SUPERFLY"	**$400**	WHAT IS
IN THIS FILM MARTIN SCORSESE, AS ONE OF ROBERT DE NIRO'S FARES, TALKS ABOUT KILLING HIS WIFE	**$600**	WHAT IS
LINDSAY WAGNER PLAYED PROFESSOR KINGSFIELD'S DAUGHTER IN THIS 1973 FILM SET AT HARVARD LAW SCHOOL	**$800**	WHAT IS
A 1975 ROBERT ALTMAN FILM CENTERS ON A MUSIC FESTIVAL & POLITICAL RALLY IN THIS TITLE CITY	**$1000**	WHAT IS

DOUBLE JEOPARDY!™

FILMS OF THE '70s

$200   WHAT IS "THE TOWERING INFERNO"?   **$200**

$400   WHAT IS BLAXPLOITATION?   **$400**

$600   WHAT IS "TAXI DRIVER"?   **$600**

$800   WHAT IS "THE PAPER CHASE"?   **$800**

$1000   WHAT IS NASHVILLE?   **$1000**

DOUBLE JEOPARDY!

OBSCURE MYTHOLOGY

ACCORDING TO AUSTRALIAN MYTH, THIS PHENOMENON SEEN IN THE SKY IS A GIANT SNAKE ARCHING ITS BODY	**$200**	WHAT IS
HUITZILOPOCHTLI, A GOD OF THESE PEOPLE, WAS SO FIERCE HE KILLED SEVERAL RELATIVES AS SOON AS HE WAS BORN	**$400**	WHO ARE
GULLINKAMBI IS THE GOLDEN COCK WHO AROUSES THE EINHER-JAR IN THIS NORSE "HALL OF THE SLAIN"	**$600**	WHAT IS
THE CHINESE GODDESS CH'ANG-O WAS TURNED INTO A TOAD, & HER SHADOW MAY BE SEEN ON THIS HEAVENLY BODY	**$800**	WHAT IS
THE EGYPTIAN GODDESS NEITH IS OFTEN DEPICTED HOLDING A SCEPTER & THIS SYMBOL OF LIFE	**$1000**	WHAT IS

DOUBLE JEOPARDY!™

OBSCURE MYTHOLOGY

$200   WHAT IS THE RAINBOW?   **$200**

$400   WHO ARE THE AZTECS?   **$400**

$600   WHAT IS VALHALLA?   **$600**

$800   WHAT IS THE MOON?   **$800**

$1000   WHAT IS AN ANKH?   **$1000**

DOUBLE JEOPARDY!

CELEBRITY RHYME TIME

SHIELDS' CHEFS	**$200**	WHAT ARE
MIDLER'S PLANES	**$400**	WHAT ARE
BRAD'S FANCY HOTEL	**$600**	WHAT IS
THE CONTENTS OF MIA'S QUIVER	**$800**	WHAT ARE
TWYLA'S STRINGED INSTRUMENTS	**$1000**	WHAT ARE

DOUBLE JEOPARDY!™

CELEBRITY RHYME TIME

$200 — WHAT ARE BROOKE'S COOKS? — $200

$400 — WHAT ARE BETTE'S JETS? — $400

$600 — WHAT IS PITT'S RITZ? — $600

$800 — WHAT ARE FARROW'S ARROWS? — $800

$1000 — WHAT ARE THARP'S HARPS? — $1000

FINAL JEOPARDY!™

WORLD CITIES

IN 1634 A SPANISH ROYAL
DECREE RECOGNIZED IT AS
THE "KEY TO THE NEW
WORLD AND THE BULWARK
OF THE WEST INDIES"

WHAT IS

FINAL JEOPARDY!

WORLD CITIES

WHAT IS HAVANA (CUBA)?

JEOPARDY!

THE FAB (18)50s

ON JUNE 16, 1858 LINCOLN DECLARED THAT ONE OF THESE "DIVIDED AGAINST ITSELF CANNOT STAND"	**$100**	WHAT IS
IN 1852 THE ALBANY EVENING JOURNAL COINED THIS WORD TO BE USED INSTEAD OF "TELEGRAPHIC DISPATCH"	**$200**	WHAT IS
DICKENS TACKLED THE FRENCH REVOLUTION IN THIS 1859 WORK	**$300**	WHAT IS
THE 1857 SUPREME COURT DECISION CONCERNING THIS ONETIME SLAVE PERMITTED SLAVERY IN ALL U.S. TERRITORIES	**$400**	WHO IS
THE TREATY OF PARIS OF 1856 ENDING THIS WAR FORCED RUSSIA TO GIVE UP THE MOUTH OF THE DANUBE TO TURKEY	**$500**	WHAT IS

JEOPARDY!™

THE FAB (18)50s

$100   WHAT IS
A HOUSE?   **$100**

$200   WHAT IS
TELEGRAM?   **$200**

$300   WHAT IS "A TALE OF
TWO CITIES"?   **$300**

$400   WHO IS
DRED SCOTT?   **$400**

$500   WHAT IS THE
CRIMEAN WAR?   **$500**

JEOPARDY!

SCHOOL DAZE

IN 1997 EVANSTON, ILLINOIS BRIEFLY BANNED THESE 15-MINUTE BREAKS IN ITS ELEMENTARY SCHOOLS	**$100**	WHAT ARE
IN 1993 NYC'S SCHOOLS OPENED 11 DAYS LATE AFTER EMERGENCY INSPECTION OF THIS BUILDING MATERIAL	**$200**	WHAT IS
AS THEIR NAME INDICATES, THESE SCHOOLS WERE ESTABLISHED TO "ATTRACT" STUDENTS FROM ACROSS THE CITY	**$300**	WHAT ARE
FROM LATIN FOR "SUMMON", THEY'RE CERTIFICATES GIVING PUBLIC FUNDS TO SEND KIDS TO PRIVATE SCHOOLS	**$400**	WHAT ARE
"CATHOLIC" MEANS BROADMINDED, BUT CATHOLIC SCHOOLS ARE THIS TYPE, WHICH ALSO MEANS NARROWMINDED	**$500**	WHAT IS

JEOPARDY!

SCHOOL DAZE

$100   WHAT ARE RECESSES? $100

$200   WHAT IS ASBESTOS? $200

$300   WHAT ARE MAGNET SCHOOLS? $300

$400   WHAT ARE VOUCHERS? $400

$500   WHAT IS PAROCHIAL? $500

JEOPARDY!

MOM'S THE WORD

ETHEL SKAKEL MARRIED THIS POLITICIAN IN 1950 & BORE HIM 11 CHILDREN, THE LAST AFTER HIS DEATH	**$100**	WHO IS
IN 1997 A 63-YEAR-OLD CALIFORNIA WOMAN MADE HEADLINES BY SETTING THIS GUINNESS RECORD	**$200**	WHAT IS
MIRIAM WEINSTEIN & HER HUSBAND MAX PROVIDED THIS NAME FOR A FILM COMPANY FOUNDED BY THEIR SONS IN 1980	**$300**	WHAT IS
IN 1997 BRENDA BARNES LEFT THE UPPER ECHELONS OF THIS SODA COMPANY TO BE WITH GENERATION NEXT, HER KIDS	**$400**	WHAT IS
SHE'S GWYNETH PALTROW'S MOM, & SHE PLAYED JONATHAN SILVERMAN'S MOM IN "BRIGHTON BEACH MEMOIRS"	**$500**	WHO IS

JEOPARDY!

MOM'S THE WORD

$100 WHO IS ROBERT F. KENNEDY? **$100**

$200 WHAT IS OLDEST (NEW) MOTHER? **$200**

$300 WHAT IS MIRAMAX? **$300**

$400 WHAT IS PEPSI-COLA (NORTH AMERICA)? **$400**

$500 WHO IS BLYTHE DANNER? **$500**

JEOPARDY!™

INDIANAGRAMS

GRAY	**$100**	WHAT IS
I SAIL IN A POND	**$200**	WHAT IS
BEST HOUND	**$300**	WHAT IS
VILLA SEVEN	**$400**	WHAT IS
RUE THE RATE	**$500**	WHAT IS

JEOPARDY!

INDIANAGRAMS

$100 — WHAT IS GARY? — $100

$200 — WHAT IS INDIANAPOLIS? — $200

$300 — WHAT IS SOUTH BEND? — $300

$400 — WHAT IS EVANSVILLE? — $400

$500 — WHAT IS TERRE HAUTE? — $500

JEOPARDY!™

THE UNITED NATIONS

Clue	Value	Response
IN 1974 THIS PLO LEADER ADDRESSED THE GENERAL ASSEMBLY WEARING A GUN & HOLSTER	**$100**	WHO IS
IN 1980 THE U.N. PASSED A RESOLUTION DEMANDING THE SOVIET UNION WITH-DRAW FROM THIS COUNTRY	**$200**	WHAT IS
IN 1950 THIS 39-STORY BUILDING WAS COMPLETED NEAR THE EAST RIVER	**$300**	WHAT IS
IN 1961 A NEW U.N. LIBRARY WAS DEDICATED & NAMED FOR THIS SWEDISH SECRETARY-GENERAL	**$400**	WHO IS
THIS BLACK AMERICAN HELPED WRITE THE U.N. CHARTER & WENT ON TO WIN A NOBEL PEACE PRIZE	**$500**	WHO IS

JEOPARDY!

THE UNITED NATIONS

$100	WHO IS YASIR ARAFAT?	**$100**
$200	WHAT IS AFGHANISTAN?	**$200**
$300	WHAT IS THE SECRETARIAT?	**$300**
$400	WHO IS DAG HAMMARSKJOLD?	**$400**
$500	WHO IS RALPH BUNCHE?	**$500**

JEOPARDY!

UNDER THE COVERS

SIOUXSIE & THE BANSHEES' COVER VERSION OF THIS GROUP'S "DEAR PRUDENCE" HIT NO. 3 IN THE U.K.	**$100**	WHO ARE
THIS DEXYS MIDNIGHT RUNNERS NO. 1 HIT WAS SUCCESSFULLY COVERED BY SKA BAND SAVE FERRIS	**$200**	WHAT IS
IN 1996 THE FUGEES UPDATED HER 1973 HIT "KILLING ME SOFTLY"	**$300**	WHO IS
THIS WELSH POP LEGEND TEAMED WITH THE ART OF NOISE TO HAVE A HIT WITH PRINCE'S SONG "KISS"	**$400**	WHO IS
DOLLY PARTON & 10,000 MANIACS HAVE RIDDEN TO SUCCESS WITH VERSIONS OF THIS CAT STEVENS SONG	**$500**	WHAT IS

JEOPARDY!

UNDER THE COVERS

$100	WHO ARE THE BEATLES?	$100
$200	WHAT IS "COME ON EILEEN"?	$200
$300	WHO IS ROBERTA FLACK?	$300
$400	WHO IS TOM JONES?	$400
$500	WHAT IS "PEACE TRAIN"?	$500

DOUBLE JEOPARDY!

FAMOUS FRENCHMEN

THIS MARINE EXPLORER WON AN OSCAR FOR THE 1956 DOCUMENTARY "THE SILENT WORLD"	**$200**	WHO IS
IN 1619 THIS MATH WHIZ COULD HAVE SAID, "I THINK, THEREFORE I AM JOINING THE DUKE OF BAVARIA'S ARMY"	**$400**	WHO IS
THIS CARDINAL, "THE RED EMINENCE", MADE HIS ENEMIES SEE RED, SO HE WAS BANISHED IN 1617	**$600**	WHO IS
PLAYWRIGHT JEAN-BAPTISTE POQUELIN BEGAN USING THIS 1-WORD STAGE NAME IN THE 1640S	**$800**	WHAT IS
THIS DIRECTOR'S FILMS INCLUDE "JULES AND JIM" & THE AUTOBIOGRAPHICAL "THE 400 BLOWS"	**$1000**	WHO IS

DOUBLE JEOPARDY!

FAMOUS FRENCHMEN

$200 — WHO IS JACQUES (-YVES) COUSTEAU? — **$200**

$400 — WHO IS RENE DESCARTES? — **$400**

$600 — WHO IS CARDINAL RICHELIEU? — **$600**

$800 — WHAT IS MOLIERE? — **$800**

$1000 — WHO IS FRANCOIS TRUFFAUT? — **$1000**

DOUBLE JEOPARDY!

MUSICAL INSTRUMENTS

THE MOUTHPIECE OF AN OBOE CONTAINS A DOUBLE ONE	**$200**	WHAT IS
A FLAMENCO DANCER SHOULD ALSO BE ACCOMPLISHED ON THESE PERCUSSION INSTRUMENTS	**$400**	WHAT ARE
HEARD IN STRING QUARTETS, IT'S 1-3 INCHES LONGER THAN A VIOLIN	**$600**	WHAT IS
A TYPE OF TRAP FOR ANIMALS, OR A TYPE OF SIDE DRUM	**$800**	WHAT IS
POPULARIZED BY LIONEL HAMPTON, YOU HAVE TO PLUG IT IN FIRST	**$1000**	WHAT IS

DOUBLE JEOPARDY!

MUSICAL INSTRUMENTS

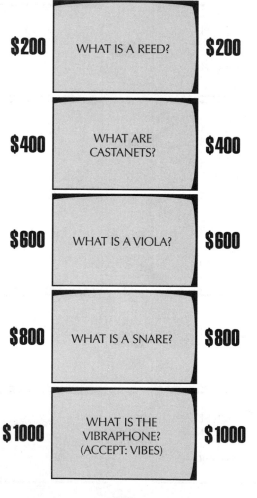

$200 — WHAT IS A REED? — $200

$400 — WHAT ARE CASTANETS? — $400

$600 — WHAT IS A VIOLA? — $600

$800 — WHAT IS A SNARE? — $800

$1000 — WHAT IS THE VIBRAPHONE? (ACCEPT: VIBES) — $1000

DOUBLE JEOPARDY!

BASEBALL

Clue	Value	Response
THE AWARD FOR OUTSTANDING PITCHER IN EACH LEAGUE IS NAMED FOR THIS OLD-TIME 500-GAME WINNER	**$200**	WHO IS
THIS SEATTLE MARINER WAS NAMED MVP OF THE 1992 ALL-STAR GAME; HIS FATHER WON THE AWARD IN 1980	**$400**	WHO IS
THIS CENTER FIELDER HIT A CAREER RECORD 18 WORLD SERIES HOME RUNS—3 MORE THAN BABE RUTH	**$600**	WHO IS
IN 1930 HACK WILSON SET A LONG-STANDING RECORD WITH 190 OF THESE	**$800**	WHAT ARE
THIS YANKEE RELIEF PITCHER WAS MVP OF THE 1999 WORLD SERIES	**$1000**	WHO IS

DOUBLE JEOPARDY!

BASEBALL

$200	WHO IS CY YOUNG?	**$200**
$400	WHO IS KEN GRIFFEY JR.?	**$400**
$600	WHO IS MICKEY MANTLE?	**$600**
$800	WHAT ARE RBIs? (ACCEPT: RUNS BATTED IN)	**$800**
$1000	WHO IS MARIANO RIVERA?	**$1000**

DOUBLE JEOPARDY!

THEY MIGHT BE GIANTS

THIS TOWERING PHILISTINE STOOD 6 CUBITS & A SPAN, EQUAL TO 9'9"	**$200**	WHO IS
THIS 7'1", 315-POUND CENTER JOINED THE LAKERS FROM THE MAGIC IN 1996	**$400**	WHO IS
AN ANCIENT WONDER, THIS SYMBOL OF LARGENESS STOOD AT THE HARBOR OF RHODES	**$600**	WHAT IS
THIS "GIANT" OCEAN DWELLER HAS THE LARGEST EYES OF ANY CREATURE	**$800**	WHAT IS
IN THE WORKS OF RABELAIS, HE WAS GARGANTUA'S SON	**$1000**	WHO IS

DOUBLE JEOPARDY!

THEY MIGHT BE GIANTS

$200 — WHO IS GOLIATH? — **$200**

$400 — WHO IS SHAQUILLE O'NEAL? — **$400**

$600 — WHAT IS THE COLOSSUS (OF RHODES)? — **$600**

$800 — WHAT IS THE (GIANT) SQUID? — **$800**

$1000 — WHO IS PANTAGRUEL? — **$1000**

DOUBLE JEOPARDY!

ANCIENT TRAVEL GUIDE

VISIT HERE & ENJOY MEDITERRANEAN CUISINE, BEAUTIFUL WOMEN & A HUGE WOODEN HORSE DONATED BY THE GREEKS	**$200**	WHAT IS
NO BULL, CRETE WILL A-MAZE YOU AS YOU WANDER THROUGH THE LABYRINTH, THIS CREATURE'S LAIR	**$400**	WHAT IS
LUSCIOUS GARDENS HANGING FOR YOUR PLEASURE AWAIT YOU IN THIS ANCIENT CITY ON THE EUPHRATES	**$600**	WHAT IS
JOIN US IN THIS AFRICAN HOT SPOT & WE'LL SUPPLY ELEPHANTS & A TOUR OF HANNIBAL'S BIRTHPLACE	**$800**	WHAT IS
BARREN ACCOMMODATIONS, BUT PLENTY OF EXERCISE & MILITARY DRILL IN THIS CAPITAL OF LACONIA	**$1000**	WHAT IS

DOUBLE JEOPARDY!

ANCIENT TRAVEL GUIDE

$200   WHAT IS TROY?   **$200**

$400   WHAT IS THE MINOTAUR?   **$400**

$600   WHAT IS BABYLON?   **$600**

$800   WHAT IS CARTHAGE?   **$800**

$1000   WHAT IS SPARTA? (ACCEPT: LACEDAEMON)   **$1000**

DOUBLE JEOPARDY!

PROVERBS

IT "CATCHES THE WORM"	**$200**	WHAT IS
THERE'S NOT ONLY ONE "TO EVERY RULE", IT ALSO "PROVES THE RULE"	**$400**	WHAT IS
PROVERBIALLY, "YOU CAN LEAD A HORSE TO WATER, BUT YOU CAN'T" DO THIS	**$600**	WHAT IS
GEORGE BERNARD SHAW WAS THE FIRST TO OBSERVE THAT "HE WHO CAN DOES; HE WHO CANNOT" DOES THIS	**$800**	WHAT IS
THE SAYING "THERE IS NOTHING NEW UNDER THE SUN" IS A VARIATION OF A PROVERB IN THIS OLD TESTAMENT BOOK	**$1000**	WHAT IS

DOUBLE JEOPARDY!

PROVERBS

$200	WHAT IS THE EARLY BIRD?	**$200**
$400	WHAT IS (THE) EXCEPTION?	**$400**
$600	WHAT IS "MAKE HIM DRINK"?	**$600**
$800	WHAT IS TEACHES?	**$800**
$1000	WHAT IS ECCLESIASTES?	**$1000**

FINAL JEOPARDY!

1990s BESTSELLERS

IN 1998, 35 YEARS AFTER
HER DEATH, SHE WAS THE
SUBJECT OF A NEW
COLLECTION OF POEMS
BY HER HUSBAND

WHO IS

FINAL JEOPARDY!

1990s BESTSELLERS

WHO IS SYLVIA PLATH?

JEOPARDY!™

A GLADIATOR'S LIFE

TRANSLATED FROM LATIN, "GLADIATOR" MEANS A "MAN OF" THIS WEAPON	**$100**	WHAT IS
LIKE CERTAIN MOVIE CRITICS, IT'S BELIEVED SPECTATORS DECIDED GLADIATORS' FATE BY DISPLAYING THIS	**$200**	WHAT IS
IT'S THE BETTER KNOWN NAME FOR THE FLAVIAN AMPHITHEATER WHERE GLADIATORS FOUGHT	**$300**	WHAT IS
THIS 3-PRONGED GLADIATORIAL WEAPON WAS A FAVORITE OF THE GOD NEPTUNE	**$400**	WHAT IS
BEFORE HE LED A SLAVE REVOLT IN THE 70s B.C., HE WAS A GLADIATOR IN TRAINING	**$500**	WHO IS

JEOPARDY!™

A GLADIATOR'S LIFE

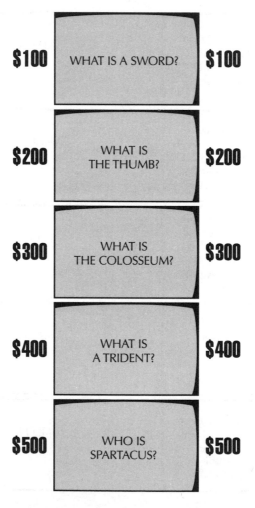

$100   WHAT IS A SWORD? $100

$200   WHAT IS THE THUMB? $200

$300   WHAT IS THE COLOSSEUM? $300

$400   WHAT IS A TRIDENT? $400

$500   WHO IS SPARTACUS? $500

JEOPARDY!

CONNECTICUTIES

IN 1993 THIS FAIRFIELD-BORN ACTRESS STARRED WITH HUSBAND DENNIS QUAID IN "FLESH AND BONE"	**$100**	WHO IS
THIS FEMALE STAR OF "THE BIG CHILL" & "DANGEROUS LIAISONS" IS A 12th-GENERATION NEW ENGLANDER	**$200**	WHO IS
IN 1933 MARION BERGERON OF WEST HAVEN BECAME THE FIRST & ONLY CONNECTICUTIE CROWNED THIS	**$300**	WHAT IS
THIS MAN FROM WATERBURY HAS MADE SOME MOUTHS WATER IN HIS ROLE ON "THE PRACTICE"	**$400**	WHO IS
THIS STAR OF TV'S "CHINA BEACH" IS THE HEIRESS TO A TOILET FLUSH VALVE FORTUNE	**$500**	WHO IS

JEOPARDY!™

CONNECTICUTIES

$100	WHO IS MEG RYAN?	$100
$200	WHO IS GLENN CLOSE?	$200
$300	WHAT IS MISS AMERICA?	$300
$400	WHO IS DYLAN McDERMOTT?	$400
$500	WHO IS DANA DELANY?	$500

JEOPARDY!

THE PLANE TRUTH

WHEN LINDBERGH TOOK THIS PLANE ON A TEST FLIGHT, HE SET A CALIFORNIA-TO-NEW YORK SPEED RECORD	**$100**	WHAT IS
HE FLEW HIS FAMOUS GUESTS TO SAN SIMEON IN A VULTEE V1-A	**$200**	WHO IS
IN THE LATE '60s BOEING DEVELOPED THE FIRST JUMBO JET & GAVE IT THIS NUMBER	**$300**	WHAT IS
IN 1954 THE CONVAIR XFY-1 BECAME THE FIRST PLANE TO MAKE A VTOL—THIS KIND OF TAKE-OFF & LANDING	**$400**	WHAT IS
INTRODUCED IN 1944, THIS GERMAN COMPANY'S ME262 WAS THE FIRST JET COMBAT PLANE	**$500**	WHAT IS

JEOPARDY!

THE PLANE TRUTH

$100	WHAT IS THE SPIRIT OF ST. LOUIS?	$100
$200	WHO IS WILLIAM RANDOLPH HEARST?	$200
$300	WHAT IS 747?	$300
$400	WHAT IS VERTICAL?	$400
$500	WHAT IS MESSERSCHMITT?	$500

JEOPARDY!™

GAME SHOW WOMEN

BEFORE BEING ON "SALE OF THE CENTURY", SUMMER BARTHOLOMEW PRECEDED VANNA WHITE ON THIS GAME	**$100**	WHAT IS
GENA LEE NOLIN OF "THE PRICE IS RIGHT" MOVED ON TO LIFE-GUARD DUTY ON THIS SYNDICATED SERIES	**$200**	WHAT IS
SHOW IN COMMON TO JENNY McCARTHY & CARMEN ELECTRA	**$300**	WHAT IS
MARK GOODSON'S DAUGHTER MARJORIE WAS A MODEL ON THE "CLASSIC" VERSION OF THIS GAME	**$400**	WHAT IS
KC WINKLER, BECKY PRICE & RUTA LEE APPEARED ON VARIOUS VERSIONS OF THIS DICE GAME	**$500**	WHAT IS

JEOPARDY!™

GAME SHOW WOMEN

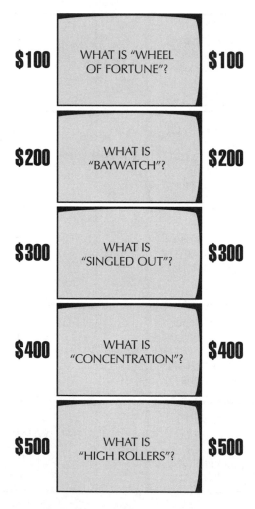

$100 — WHAT IS "WHEEL OF FORTUNE"? — $100

$200 — WHAT IS "BAYWATCH"? — $200

$300 — WHAT IS "SINGLED OUT"? — $300

$400 — WHAT IS "CONCENTRATION"? — $400

$500 — WHAT IS "HIGH ROLLERS"? — $500

JEOPARDY!

EXPLORATION

THE FAMOUS GREETING "DR. LIVINGSTONE, I PRESUME?" IS ATTRIBUTED TO HIM	**$100**	WHO IS
A CITY IN WHAT IS NOW THIS STATE WAS NAMED TO HONOR JULIEN DUBUQUE, 23 YEARS AFTER HIS DEATH	**$200**	WHAT IS
THIS MAN, WHOSE EXPEDITION WAS SECOND TO THE SOUTH POLE, JOINED THE ROYAL NAVY IN 1880, THE YEAR HE TURNED 12	**$300**	WHO IS
IN 1498, THIS PORTUGUESE EXPLORER RECRUITED A PILOT IN EAST AFRICA TO HELP HIM FIND INDIA	**$400**	WHO IS
GONZALO JIMENEZ DE QUESADA FOUNDED BOGOTA BETWEEN 2 TRIPS TO FIND THIS MYTHICAL GOLDEN CITY	**$500**	WHAT IS

JEOPARDY!

EXPLORATION

$100 | WHO IS HENRY MORTON STANLEY? | **$100**

$200 | WHAT IS IOWA? | **$200**

$300 | WHO IS ROBERT F. SCOTT? | **$300**

$400 | WHO IS VASCO DA GAMA? | **$400**

$500 | WHAT IS EL DORADO? | **$500**

JEOPARDY!

THE APOSTROPHE STANDS FOR ...

IN THE WORD WOULDN'T	**$100**	WHAT IS
IN THE WORD DANCIN'	**$200**	WHAT IS
IN THE WORD YOU'VE	**$300**	WHAT IS
IN THE WORD O'ER	**$400**	WHAT IS
IN THE WORD 'TWIXT	**$500**	WHAT IS

JEOPARDY!™

THE APOSTROPHE STANDS FOR...

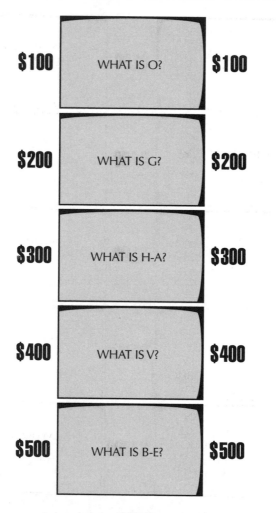

$100   WHAT IS O? $100

$200   WHAT IS G? $200

$300   WHAT IS H-A? $300

$400   WHAT IS V? $400

$500   WHAT IS B-E? $500

DOUBLE JEOPARDY!

SHORT STORY WRITERS

IT'S THOUGHT THAT THE "GIFT OF THE MAGI" AUTHOR TOOK THIS PEN NAME PARTLY FROM A PRISON GUARD	**$200**	WHO IS
THIS RUSSIAN WROTE CLASSIC SHORT STORIES LIKE "OF LOVE" AS WELL AS CLASSIC PLAYS LIKE "THE CHERRY ORCHARD"	**$400**	WHO IS
"THE CELESTIAL RAILROAD" FROM HIS "TWICE-TOLD TALES" IS A PARODY OF JOHN BUNYAN'S WORKS	**$600**	WHO IS
SUNNYSIDE, THE OLD DUTCH HOUSE HE REMODELED IN TARRYTOWN, N.Y., WAS MADE A PUBLIC SHRINE IN 1947	**$800**	WHO IS
LATE AMERICAN WHOSE TERSE STYLE IS SEEN IN COLLECTIONS LIKE "WHAT WE TALK ABOUT WHEN WE TALK ABOUT LOVE"	**$1000**	WHO IS

DOUBLE JEOPARDY!

SHORT STORY WRITERS

$200	WHO IS O. HENRY? (ACCEPT: WILLIAM SIDNEY PORTER)	**$200**
$400	WHO IS ANTON CHEKHOV?	**$400**
$600	WHO IS NATHANIEL HAWTHORNE?	**$600**
$800	WHO IS WASHINGTON IRVING?	**$800**
$1000	WHO IS RAYMOND CARVER?	**$1000**

DOUBLE JEOPARDY!

FURNITURE

OFTEN PART OF THE FRAME, IT'S THE PANEL AT THE PILLOWED END OF A BED	**$200**	WHAT IS
A HOME WORKMAN'S HOLDS TOOLS; A BALLPARK'S HOLDS THE HOME TEAM	**$400**	WHAT IS
NAMED FOR ITS INVENTOR, THIS BED THAT SWINGS UP INTO A WALL CLOSET WAS A STAPLE OF SILENT SLAPSTICK COMEDY	**$600**	WHAT IS
ONCE PAINTED OVER IN EARLY PINE FURNITURE, THESE FLAWS IN THE WOOD GRAIN ARE NOW USED FOR DECORATIVE EFFECT	**$800**	WHAT ARE
DUNCAN PHYFE WORKED IN THIS 1780-1830 PERIOD OF AMERICAN FURNITURE, BUT DIDN'T MAKE A "CASE" OF IT	**$1000**	WHAT IS

DOUBLE JEOPARDY!

FURNITURE

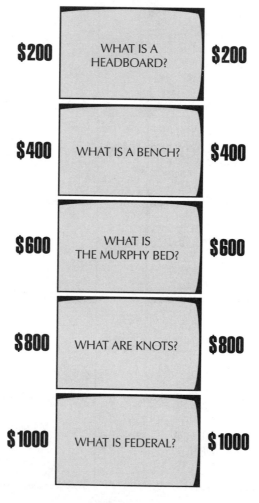

$200 — WHAT IS A HEADBOARD? — **$200**

$400 — WHAT IS A BENCH? — **$400**

$600 — WHAT IS THE MURPHY BED? — **$600**

$800 — WHAT ARE KNOTS? — **$800**

$1000 — WHAT IS FEDERAL? — **$1000**

DOUBLE JEOPARDY!

1980s FILM FACTS

SCREENWRITERS LOWELL GANZ & BABALOO MANDEL HOOKED AUDIENCES WITH THIS HANKS-HANNAH MERMAID FILM	**$200**	WHAT IS
AS ELIOT NESS, KEVIN COSTNER CLEANED UP THE MESS IN CHICAGO IN THIS 1987 FILM	**$400**	WHAT IS
HE TOOK HOME AN OSCAR FOR PLAYING THE AUTISTIC RAYMOND IN A 1988 FILM	**$600**	WHO IS
ROBIN WILLIAMS SAILED INTO MOVIE STARDOM AS THIS TITLE CHARACTER OPPOSITE SHELLEY DUVALL AS OLIVE OYL	**$800**	WHAT IS
THIS OFFBEAT DIRECTOR CAST HIMSELF AS A NUTTY PSYCHIATRIST IN HIS OWN FILM "HAIRSPRAY"	**$1000**	WHO IS

DOUBLE JEOPARDY!

1980s FILM FACTS

$200	WHAT IS "SPLASH"?	**$200**
$400	WHAT IS "THE UNTOUCHABLES"?	**$400**
$600	WHO IS DUSTIN HOFFMAN?	**$600**
$800	WHAT IS POPEYE?	**$800**
$1000	WHO IS JOHN WATERS?	**$1000**

DOUBLE JEOPARDY!

WIINSTON CHURCHILL

EXCEPT FOR 2 YEARS, CHURCHILL SERVED IN THIS "HOUSE" FROM 1900 TO HIS 1964 RESIGNATION	**$200**	WHAT IS
THE "FEW" IN WINSTON'S QUOTE, "NEVER IN THE FIELD OF HUMAN CONFLICT WAS SO MUCH OWED BY SO MANY TO SO FEW"	**$400**	WHAT IS
CHURCHILL'S MOTHER, BORN JENNIE JEROME, WAS A NATIVE OF THIS COUNTRY	**$600**	WHAT IS
CHURCHILL DECLARED THAT AS PRIME MINISTER HE HAD "NOTHING TO OFFER BUT BLOOD, TOIL" & THESE 2 FLUIDS	**$800**	WHAT ARE
CHURCHILL WAS DESCENDED FROM JOHN CHURCHILL, THE FIRST DUKE OF THIS	**$1000**	WHAT IS

DOUBLE JEOPARDY!

WIINSTON CHURCHILL

$200	WHAT IS THE HOUSE OF COMMONS?	**$200**
$400	WHAT IS THE RAF? (ACCEPT: ROYAL AIR FORCE)	**$400**
$600	WHAT IS THE UNITED STATES?	**$600**
$800	WHAT ARE TEARS & SWEAT?	**$800**
$1000	WHAT IS MARLBOROUGH?	**$1000**

DOUBLE JEOPARDY!

GREEK LETTERS

GREEK LETTER YOU NEED TO KNOW TO FIGURE OUT THE AREA OF A CIRCLE	$200	WHAT IS
THIS FOURTH GREEK LETTER IS IN THE TITLE OF HELEN REDDY'S SECOND NO. 1 HIT	$400	WHAT IS
IT'S THE FINAL NAME IN WATCH BRANDS	$600	WHAT IS
COMPUTER GAMES & PROGRAMS UNDERGO THIS TEST PERIOD TO WORK OUT BUGS BEFORE THEIR FINAL RETAIL RELEASE	$800	WHAT IS
EXPLORE AMERICAN SAMOA & YOU'LL COME ACROSS THIS ISLAND THAT'LL SUIT YOU TO A "T"	$1000	WHAT IS

DOUBLE JEOPARDY!

GREEK LETTERS

$200	WHAT IS PI?	**$200**
$400	WHAT IS DELTA?	**$400**
$600	WHAT IS OMEGA?	**$600**
$800	WHAT IS BETA (TESTING)?	**$800**
$1000	WHAT IS TAU?	**$1000**

DOUBLE JEOPARDY!

GIVE IT A MYTH

THIS RULER WITH A PLANETARY NAME RARELY, IF EVER, LEAVES HIS DOMAIN, THE UNDERWORLD	**$200**	WHO IS
PERSEUS PROVED THIS GORGON WASN'T IMMORTAL	**$400**	WHO IS
ADD ONE MORE LETTER TO EOS & YOU'LL GET THIS GOD OF LOVE	**$600**	WHO IS
THE GODDESSES APHRODITE & PERSE-PHONE BOTH LOVED THIS YOUTH WHOSE NAME IS APPLIED TO ANY HANDSOME MAN	**$800**	WHO IS
YOU COULD SAY THIS KING OF EPHRYA HAD QUITE ENOUGH ROLLING ROCK	**$1000**	WHO IS

DOUBLE JEOPARDY!

GIVE IT A MYTH

$200	WHO IS PLUTO?	**$200**
$400	WHO IS MEDUSA?	**$400**
$600	WHO IS EROS?	**$600**
$800	WHO IS ADONIS?	**$800**
$1000	WHO IS SISYPHUS?	**$1000**

FINAL JEOPARDY!

SINGERS

HE FIRST RECORDED IN
1939, "RETIRED" IN 1971,
RETURNED & HAD A TOP 10
ALBUM IN 1993

WHO IS

FINAL JEOPARDY!

SINGERS

WHO IS FRANK SINATRA?

JEOPARDY!

HOOKED ON PHOENIX

Clue	Value	Response
PERHAPS THIS TEAM'S GREATEST GAME EVER WAS A TRIPLE-OVERTIME LOSS TO THE CELTICS IN THE 1976 FINALS	**$100**	WHO ARE
THE NAME OF THE RIVER THAT FLOWS THROUGH PHOENIX, IT'S ALSO FOUND IN THE NAME OF A UTAH LAKE	**$200**	WHAT IS
PHOENIX' FIREFIGHTING MUSEUM ISN'T CALLED THE HALL OF FAME BUT THE HALL OF THIS	**$300**	WHAT IS
THE ARIZONA BILTMORE WAS INSPIRED BY THE DESIGNS OF THIS MAN WHO LIVED & WORKED AT NEARBY TALIESIN WEST	**$400**	WHO IS
BY GUM, THE MANSION BUILT BY THIS CHEWING GUM MOGUL IS A NATIONAL HISTORIC LANDMARK	**$500**	WHO IS

JEOPARDY!

HOOKED ON PHOENIX

$100 — WHO ARE THE (PHOENIX) SUNS? — $100

$200 — WHAT IS SALT (RIVER)? — $200

$300 — WHAT IS (THE HALL OF) FLAME? — $300

$400 — WHO IS FRANK LLOYD WRIGHT? — $400

$500 — WHO IS WILLIAM WRIGLEY (JR.)? — $500

JEOPARDY!™

THE '60s

Clue	Value	Response
THIS CITY'S KING'S ROAD & CARNABY STREET WERE HOT SPOTS OF '60s FASHION	**$100**	WHAT IS
MOVIE RATING GIVEN "THE KILLING OF SISTER GEORGE" IN 1968 & "MIDNIGHT COWBOY" IN 1969	**$200**	WHAT IS
THIS COUPLE, WHO APPEARED NUDE ON THEIR 1968 RECORD COVER, WED IN 1969	**$300**	WHO ARE
POLICE WARNINGS STEM FROM THE 1966 SUPREME COURT CASE OF THIS MAN V. ARIZONA	**$400**	WHO IS
IT TOOK 18 DAYS TO REPLACE THIS LATE POPE IN 1963	**$500**	WHO IS

JEOPARDY!

THE '60s

$100 WHAT IS LONDON? **$100**

$200 WHAT IS X? **$200**

$300 WHO ARE JOHN LENNON & YOKO ONO? **$300**

$400 WHO IS ERNESTO MIRANDA? **$400**

$500 WHO IS JOHN XXIII? **$500**

JEOPARDY!

GOOD DEEDS

IN 1982 LENNY SKUTNICK RESCUED A PASSENGER ON A CRASHED 737 FROM THIS D.C. RIVER	$100	WHAT IS
FITTINGLY, CNN BROKE THE NEWS IN 1997 WHEN THIS MAN DECIDED TO GIVE $1 BILLION TO THE U.N.	$200	WHO IS
JODY WILLIAMS WON A 1997 NOBEL PEACE PRIZE FOR HER EFFORTS TO BAN THESE WEAPONS	$300	WHAT ARE
IN 1997, 5 DECADES LATE, 7 BLACK SOLDIERS RECEIVED THIS HIGHEST AWARD FOR BRAVERY DURING WWII	$400	WHAT IS
JAPANESE CONSUL CHIUNE SUGIHARA, WHO SAVED HUN-DREDS OF JEWS IN WWII, BEARS THE TITLE "RIGHTEOUS" THIS	$500	WHAT IS

187

JEOPARDY!

GOOD DEEDS

$100 WHAT IS THE POTOMAC? **$100**

$200 WHO IS TED TURNER? **$200**

$300 WHAT ARE LANDMINES? **$300**

$400 WHAT IS THE (CONGRESSIONAL) MEDAL OF HONOR? **$400**

$500 WHAT IS GENTILE? (ACCEPT: AMONG THE NATIONS) **$500**

JEOPARDY!

MEL BROOKS MOVIES

ACCORDING TO THE TITLE OF MEL'S 1995 FILM, THIS VAMPIRE IS "DEAD AND LOVING IT"	**$100**	WHO IS
IT'S TWUE! IT'S TWUE! MADELINE KAHN PLAYED SINGER LILI VON SHTUPP IN THIS UPROARIOUS WESTERN	**$200**	WHAT IS
IN THIS FILM ZERO MOSTEL SCHEMES TO SELL 25,000 PERCENT OF A PLAY HE'S PUTTING ON	**$300**	WHAT IS
TERI GARR PLAYED A SEXY BLONDE NAMED INGA & PETER BOYLE WAS A MONSTER IN THIS FILM	**$400**	WHAT IS
"HISTORY OF THE WORLD—PART I" FEATURED MEL AS MOSES, TORQUEMADA & THE WAITER AT THIS BIBLICAL DINNER	**$500**	WHAT IS

JEOPARDY!™

MEL BROOKS MOVIES

$100	WHO IS DRACULA?	**$100**
$200	WHAT IS "BLAZING SADDLES"?	**$200**
$300	WHAT IS "THE PRODUCERS"?	**$300**
$400	WHAT IS "YOUNG FRANKENSTEIN"?	**$400**
$500	WHAT IS THE LAST SUPPER?	**$500**

JEOPARDY!

ODD WORDS

Clue	Value	Response
PEOPLE WERE AURIFIED BY KING MIDAS, MEANING HE TURNED THEM INTO THIS	**$100**	WHAT IS
THIS INSECT STORES POLLEN IN A CORBICULA, A LITTLE BASKET ON ITS BODY	**$200**	WHAT IS
A WOUBIT IS A HAIRY ONE OF THESE, MOST OFTEN THE ONE THAT BECOMES A TIGER MOTH	**$300**	WHAT IS
TO CANTILLATE IS TO DO THIS (MAYBE TO AN OLD GREGORIAN ONE)	**$400**	WHAT IS
A MAIKO IS AN APPRENTICE ONE OF THESE WOMEN WHO ENTERTAIN MEN IN JAPAN	**$500**	WHAT IS

JEOPARDY!™

ODD WORDS

$100	WHAT IS GOLD?	**$100**
$200	WHAT IS A BEE?	**$200**
$300	WHAT IS A CATERPILLAR?	**$300**
$400	WHAT IS CHANT?	**$400**
$500	WHAT IS A GEISHA?	**$500**

JEOPARDY!

NICKNAMES

IVAN I WAS IVAN MONEYBAG, IVAN II WAS IVAN THE RED, & IVAN IV WAS THIS	**$100**	WHAT IS
THIS "LUCKY" MOBSTER'S LUCK RAN OUT AT THE NAPLES AIRPORT ON JANUARY 26, 1962	**$200**	WHO IS
BUCK TAYLOR, A STAR OF BUFFALO BILL'S WILD WEST SHOW, EARNED THIS "ROYAL" NICK-NAME BEFORE ROY ROGERS	**$300**	WHAT IS
WE PRESUME THIS VIRGINIAN FELT GOOD ABOUT HIS NICKNAME, "THE ERA-OF-GOOD-FEELING PRESIDENT"	**$400**	WHO IS
SOME CALLED THIS "MESSIAH" COMPOSER "THE THUNDERBOLT" AFTER MOZART SAID HE STRUCK LIKE ONE	**$500**	WHO IS

JEOPARDY!™

NICKNAMES

$100   WHAT IS IVAN THE TERRIBLE? $100

$200   WHO IS CHARLES "LUCKY" LUCIANO? (ACCEPT: LUCIANA) $200

$300   WHAT IS "KING OF THE COWBOYS"? $300

$400   WHO IS JAMES MONROE? $400

$500   WHO IS GEORGE FREDERICK HANDEL? $500

DOUBLE JEOPARDY!

HISTORY BOOKS

THIS 1997 STEVEN SPIELBERG FILM RENEWED INTEREST IN WILLIAM OWEN'S HISTORY "BLACK MUTINY"	**$200**	WHAT IS
SHELBY FOOTE'S 3-VOLUME CIVIL WAR HISTORY ENDS WITH THE TOME "RED RIVER TO" THIS SURRENDER SITE	**$400**	WHAT IS
STEPHEN AMBROSE'S "UNDAUNTED COURAGE" EXPLORES THE FRIENDSHIP OF MERIWETHER LEWIS & THIS PRESIDENT	**$600**	WHO IS
BARBARA TUCHMAN WON HER FIRST PULITZER FOR THIS HISTORY OF THE BEGINNING OF WORLD WAR I	**$800**	WHAT IS
THE AUTHOR OF "THE GALLIC WAR" WROTE IN THE THIRD PERSON, REFERRING TO HIMSELF BY THIS ONE-WORD TITLE	**$1000**	WHAT IS

DOUBLE JEOPARDY!

HISTORY BOOKS

$200	WHAT IS "AMISTAD"?	**$200**
$400	WHAT IS APPOMATTOX?	**$400**
$600	WHO IS THOMAS JEFFERSON?	**$600**
$800	WHAT IS "THE GUNS OF AUGUST"?	**$800**
$1000	WHAT IS CAESAR?	**$1000**

DOUBLE JEOPARDY!

PHONY EXPRESS

THE "CON" IN "CON MAN" IS SHORT FOR THIS	**$200**	WHAT IS
PYRITE GOT THIS NAME WHEN MANY PROSPECTORS MISTOOK IT FOR A MORE VALUABLE MINERAL	**$400**	WHAT IS
POSING AS ARABS WITH LOTS OF CASH, THE FBI CAUGHT 7 MEMBERS OF CONGRESS IN THIS 1970s STING OPERATION	**$600**	WHAT IS
HE SERVED TIME FOR FRAUD AFTER WRITING A FAKE HOWARD HUGHES BIOGRAPHY	**$800**	WHO IS
DUMMKOPFS! THIS GERMAN NEWS-MAGAZINE PAID MILLIONS FOR FORGED DIARIES OF ADOLF HITLER IN 1983	**$1000**	WHAT IS

DOUBLE JEOPARDY!

PHONY EXPRESS

$200	WHAT IS CONFIDENCE?	**$200**
$400	WHAT IS FOOL'S GOLD?	**$400**
$600	WHAT IS ABSCAM? (ACCEPT: ARAB SCAM)	**$600**
$800	WHO IS CLIFFORD IRVING?	**$800**
$1000	WHAT IS STERN MAGAZINE?	**$1000**

DOUBLE JEOPARDY!

BRIT ROCK

Clue	Value	Response
MICK JAGGER FIRST MET THIS FUTURE BANDMATE IN PRIMARY SCHOOL WHEN THEY WERE 7	**$200**	WHO IS
IN 1984 THEY HAD A HIT WITH THE BOUNCY "WAKE ME UP BEFORE YOU GO-GO"	**$400**	WHAT IS
THIS "DARK" HEAVY METAL BAND OF THE 1970S CONSISTED OF BILL WARD, TONY IOMMI, GEEZER BUTLER & OZZY OSBOURNE	**$600**	WHAT IS
THIS BAND BEST KNOWN FOR THEIR 1985 HIT "WALKING ON SUNSHINE" WON THE 1997 EUROVISION SONG CONTEST	**$800**	WHAT IS
THIS OFTEN-GLOOMY GROUP HAS LONG BEEN LED BY LIPSTICK-SPORTING ROBERT SMITH	**$1000**	WHAT IS

DOUBLE JEOPARDY!

BRIT ROCK

$200 — WHO IS KEITH RICHARDS? (ACCEPT: KEITH RICHARD) — $200

$400 — WHAT IS WHAM! (UK)? — $400

$600 — WHAT IS BLACK SABBATH? — $600

$800 — WHAT IS KATRINA & THE WAVES? — $800

$1000 — WHAT IS THE CURE? — $1000

DOUBLE JEOPARDY!

TOUGH SHAKESPEARE

SHYLOCK IS OUTWITTED IN COURT IN ACT IV OF THIS PLAY	**$200**	WHAT IS
THIS "TEMPEST" MAGIC-MAKER HAS A DAUGHTER NAMED MIRANDA & A SPRITELY SERVANT NAMED ARIEL	**$400**	WHO IS
PERSON TO WHOM HAMLET ADDRESSES HIS DYING WORDS	**$600**	WHO IS
ACT III OF THIS PLAY OPENS INSIDE KING PRIAM'S PALACE IN TROY	**$800**	WHAT IS
MISTRESS FORD & MISTRESS PAGE ARE THE SAUCY SPOUSES WHO TRICK & TORMENT FALSTAFF IN THIS COMEDY	**$1000**	WHAT IS

DOUBLE JEOPARDY!

TOUGH SHAKESPEARE

$200	WHAT IS "THE MERCHANT OF VENICE"?	**$200**
$400	WHO IS PROSPERO?	**$400**
$600	WHO IS HORATIO?	**$600**
$800	WHAT IS "TROILUS AND CRESSIDA"?	**$800**
$1000	WHAT IS "THE MERRY WIVES OF WINDSOR"?	**$1000**

DOUBLE JEOPARDY!

IMPORTS

ON APRIL 14, 1927 THIS COMPANY'S FIRST CAR CAME OFF ITS GOTHENBURG, SWEDEN ASSEMBLY LINE	**$200**	WHAT IS
THIS BRAND OF WATER COMES FROM A NATURAL SPRING IN VERGEZE	**$400**	WHAT IS
IN 1900 THIS JAPANESE COMPANY BEGAN PRODUCTION OF ITS UPRIGHT PIANOS; IN 1954, ITS MOTORCYCLES	**$600**	WHAT IS
FOR 177 YEARS, UNTIL 1936, GUINNESS BREWED ALL OF ITS STOUT IN THIS CITY	**$800**	WHAT IS
GIULIANA & LUCIANO'S UNITED COLORS COMPANY	**$1000**	WHAT IS

DOUBLE JEOPARDY!

IMPORTS

$200 WHAT IS VOLVO? **$200**

$400 WHAT IS PERRIER? (ACCEPT: VITTEL) **$400**

$600 WHAT IS YAMAHA? **$600**

$800 WHAT IS DUBLIN? **$800**

$1000 WHAT IS BENETTON? **$1000**

DOUBLE JEOPARDY!

TOM SWIFTIES

IT'S THE SATIRICAL WAY TOM SAID, "I LIKE TO PRESS MY OWN CLOTHES"	**$200**	WHAT IS
IT'S THE SECRET OR ENIGMATIC WAY TOM SAID, "LET'S GO LOOK AT THOSE TOMBS"	**$400**	WHAT IS
"I SENT A FOOD PACKAGE OVERSEAS", SAID TOM THIS WAY; IT'S ALSO HOW PORCUPINES MAKE LOVE	**$600**	WHAT IS
TOM TALKS ABOUT GLOVES INTERMITTENTLY; THE WAY HE TALKS ABOUT MAGAZINES IS THIS SYNONYM	**$800**	WHAT IS
IF YOU THINK DOGGEDLY ABOUT HIS HOARSE VOICE, YOU'LL KNOW IT'S HOW TOM SAID "MUSH!"	**$1000**	WHAT IS

DOUBLE JEOPARDY!

TOM SWIFTIES

$200   WHAT IS IRONICALLY?   **$200**

$400   WHAT IS CRYPTICALLY?   **$400**

$600   WHAT IS CAREFULLY?   **$600**

$800   WHAT IS PERIODICALLY?   **$800**

$1000   WHAT IS HUSKILY?   **$1000**

FINAL JEOPARDY!

VOLCANOES

THE 5 HIGHEST VOLCANOES
ON EARTH ARE LOCATED IN
THESE MOUNTAINS

WHAT ARE

FINAL JEOPARDY!

VOLCANOES

WHAT ARE THE ANDES?

JEOPARDY!

COMING TO AMERICA

CHINESE IMMIGRANTS BEGAN TO ARRIVE IN CALIFORNIA JUST BEFORE THIS 1849 "RUSH"	**$100**	WHAT IS
IN 1634 CATHOLICS COULD FIND REFUGE IN THIS COLONY FOUNDED BY CECIL CALVERT, LORD BALTIMORE	**$200**	WHAT IS
EUROPEANS WHO CAME TO AMERICA AS THIS KIND OF "SERVANT" PROMISED TO WORK FOR YEARS TO PAY THEIR PASSAGE	**$300**	WHAT IS
PEOPLE WHO EMIGRATE TO AMERICA FROM THIS COUNTRY ARE KNOWN AS ISSEI BACK HOME	**$400**	WHAT IS
FEW OF THE PENNSYLVANIA DUTCH CAME FROM HOLLAND; MOST CAME FROM THIS PRESENT-DAY COUNTRY	**$500**	WHAT IS

JEOPARDY!

COMING TO AMERICA

$100   WHAT IS THE GOLD RUSH? $100

$200   WHAT IS MARYLAND? $200

$300   WHAT IS INDENTURED? $300

$400   WHAT IS JAPAN? $400

$500   WHAT IS GERMANY? $500

JEOPARDY!™

POWERFUL WOMEN

THE FALKLAND ISLANDS WAR TESTED THE METTLE OF THIS "IRON LADY"	**$100**	WHO IS
BILL CLINTON MADE THIS TOUGH-TALKING MIAMIAN THE NATION'S NO. 1 COP	**$200**	WHO IS
IN 1988, 9 YEARS AFTER HER FATHER'S EXECUTION, SHE BECAME PRIME MINISTER OF PAKISTAN	**$300**	WHO IS
SHE WAS PUBLISHER OF THE WASHINGTON POST DURING WATERGATE	**$400**	WHO IS
THIS NFL TEAM OWNER MOVED HER RAMS FROM CALIFORNIA TO MISSOURI	**$500**	WHO IS

JEOPARDY!

POWERFUL WOMEN

$100	WHO IS MARGARET THATCHER?	**$100**
$200	WHO IS JANET RENO?	**$200**
$300	WHO IS BENAZIR BHUTTO?	**$300**
$400	WHO IS KATHERINE GRAHAM?	**$400**
$500	WHO IS GEORGIA (ROSENBLOOM) FRONTIERE?	**$500**

JEOPARDY!

PUDDING

Clue	Value	Response
IT'S TRADITIONAL TO SERVE PLUM PUDDING ON THIS HOLIDAY, BUT DON'T PUT ANY PLUMS IN IT	**$100**	WHAT IS
IN "THROUGH THE LOOKING-GLASS", THE PUDDING REPRIMANDS THIS GIRL FOR CUTTING A SLICE OF HIM	**$200**	WHO IS
OF SPOTTED DICK, SPOTTED DARWIN OR SPOTTED DUDLEY, THE ONE THAT REALLY IS AN ENGLISH PUDDING	**$300**	WHAT IS
IN THE 1960s THIS BRAND THRILLED KIDS BY ADDING PINEAPPLE CREAM TO ITS LINE OF INSTANT PUDDINGS	**$400**	WHAT IS
LUCKILY, THIS "PUD-DING" SERVED WITH ROAST BEEF DOESN'T CONTAIN THE TERRIERS OF THE SAME NAME	**$500**	WHAT IS

JEOPARDY!

PUDDING

$100	WHAT IS CHRISTMAS?	**$100**
$200	WHO IS ALICE?	**$200**
$300	WHAT IS SPOTTED DICK?	**$300**
$400	WHAT IS JELL-O?	**$400**
$500	WHAT IS YORKSHIRE PUDDING?	**$500**

JEOPARDY!™

POP STARS

IN ADDITION TO HIS OWN BANDS, THIS GUITARIST HAS PLAYED WITH THE YARDBIRDS, CREAM & DEREK & THE DOMINOS	**$100**	WHO IS
B.B. KING MADE A GUEST APPEARANCE ON THIS GROUP'S "RATTLE AND HUM" ALBUM	**$200**	WHO ARE
"I HEARD IT THROUGH THE GRAPEVINE" THAT HE WAS ONCE A SESSION DRUMMER FOR SMOKEY ROBINSON	**$300**	WHO IS
NIRVANA DRUMMER DAVE GROHL WENT ON TO FORM THIS "COMBATIVE" BAND	**$400**	WHO ARE
JIM SEALS & THIS PARTNER TOURED WITH THE CHAMPS IN 1958, BUT DIDN'T HAVE A HIT AS A DUO UNTIL 1972	**$500**	WHO IS

JEOPARDY!

POP STARS

$100	WHO IS ERIC CLAPTON?	**$100**
$200	WHO ARE U2?	**$200**
$300	WHO IS MARVIN GAYE?	**$300**
$400	WHO ARE THE FOO FIGHTERS?	**$400**
$500	WHO IS DASH CROFTS?	**$500**

JEOPARDY!

'90s FICTION

IN 1997 IRA LEVIN DELIVERED "SON OF ROSEMARY", THE SEQUEL TO THIS NOVEL	**$100**	WHAT IS
"THIS KIND OF CERTAINTY COMES ONLY ONCE", ROBERT TELLS FRANCESCA IN THIS BESTSELLING LOVE STORY	**$200**	WHAT IS
IN "THE FOURTH K", MARIO PUZO PUT A NEW MEMBER OF THIS POLITICAL FAMILY IN THE WHITE HOUSE	**$300**	WHO ARE
THIS 1993 JAMES REDFIELD BOOK HAS BEEN DESCRIBED AS "AN ADVENTURE IN PURSUIT OF A SPIRITUAL MYSTERY"	**$400**	WHAT IS
THIS "BELOVED" AUTHOR SET HER NOVEL "PARADISE" IN THE FICTIONAL ALL-BLACK TOWN OF RUBY, OKLAHOMA	**$500**	WHO IS

JEOPARDY!™

'90s FICTION

$100	WHAT IS "ROSEMARY'S BABY"?	**$100**
$200	WHAT IS "THE BRIDGES OF MADISON COUNTY"?	**$200**
$300	WHO ARE THE KENNEDYS?	**$300**
$400	WHAT IS "THE CELESTINE PROPHECY'?	**$400**
$500	WHO IS TONI MORRISON?	**$500**

JEOPARDY!

WE THE "PEOPLE"

ACCORDING TO LYRICIST BOB MERRILL, "PEOPLE WHO NEED PEOPLE ARE" THIS	**$100**	WHAT IS
IN 1997 BILL COSBY WON FAVORITE MALE IN A NEW SERIES, HIS 15th OF THESE AWARDS	**$200**	WHAT ARE
THIS PHRASE FOR THE JEWS REFERS TO EXODUS 19:6, "YE SHALL BE UNTO ME . . . A HOLY NATION"	**$300**	WHAT IS
YOU CAN TOUR SCENIC DOWNTOWN DETROIT OR MIAMI ON THIS TYPE OF MASS TRANSIT SYSTEM	**$400**	WHAT IS
FOUNDED IN 1965, THIS "ELEVATING" ORGANIZA-TION LETS STUDENTS COMBINE INTER-NATIONAL TRAVEL & MUSICAL PERFORMANCE	**$500**	WHAT IS

JEOPARDY!™

WE THE "PEOPLE"

$100 | WHAT IS "THE LUCKIEST PEOPLE IN THE WORLD"? | **$100**

$200 | WHAT ARE THE PEOPLE'S CHOICE AWARDS? | **$200**

$300 | WHAT IS THE CHOSEN PEOPLE? | **$300**

$400 | WHAT IS A PEOPLE MOVER? | **$400**

$500 | WHAT IS UP WITH PEOPLE? | **$500**

DOUBLE JEOPARDY!

ARTISTS

IN THE 1870s, BEFORE HE MOVED TO TAHITI, HE WAS STRONGLY INFLUENCED BY CAMILLE PISSARRO	**$200**	WHO IS
YOU CAN SEE HIS UNFINISHED "RONDANINI PIETA" AT THE CASTELLO SFORZESCO IN MILAN	**$400**	WHO IS
A NEW MUSEUM DEVOTED TO THIS FLOWERS-&-SKULLS ARTIST OPENED IN SANTA FE IN 1997	**$600**	WHO IS
IN 1888 HE PAINTED A "CAFE TERRACE AT NIGHT" AS WELL AS "THE NIGHT CAFE"	**$800**	WHO IS
PAINTER MARGARETT SARGENT, WHO LIVED UNTIL 1978, WAS A COUSIN OF THIS SOCIETY PORTRAITIST	**$1000**	WHO IS

DOUBLE JEOPARDY!

ARTISTS

$200	WHO IS PAUL GAUGUIN?	**$200**
$400	WHO IS MICHELANGELO?	**$400**
$600	WHO IS GEORGIA O'KEEFFE?	**$600**
$800	WHO IS VINCENT VAN GOGH?	**$800**
$1000	WHO IS JOHN SINGER SARGENT?	**$1000**

DOUBLE JEOPARDY!

STRIFE WITH FATHER

SHE WHACKED HER STEPMOM, SAW WHAT SHE'D DONE, THEN "GAVE HER FATHER 41"	**$200**	WHO IS
THANKS TO AN ANGEL, ABRAHAM DIDN'T MAKE HIM THE ULTIMATE SACRIFICE	**$400**	WHO IS
IT'S PRETTY "COMPLEX" HOW HE MANAGED TO KILL HIS FATHER, SOLVE THE SPHINX' RIDDLE & MARRY HIS MOTHER	**$600**	WHO IS
IN 1989 JOSE & KITTY PAID DEARLY BECAUSE THESE 2 ALLEGEDLY COULDN'T WAIT FOR THEIR BEVERLY HILLS INHERITANCE	**$800**	WHO ARE
EXECUTED IN UTAH IN 1977, HE TOLD HIS BROTHER THAT THEIR FATHER WAS THE FIRST PERSON HE EVER WANTED TO MURDER	**$1000**	WHO IS

223

DOUBLE JEOPARDY!

STRIFE WITH FATHER

$200 — WHO IS LIZZIE BORDEN? — $200

$400 — WHO IS ISAAC? — $400

$600 — WHO IS OEDIPUS? — $600

$800 — WHO ARE LYLE & ERIK MENENDEZ? — $800

$1000 — WHO IS GARY GILMORE? — $1000

DOUBLE JEOPARDY!

TOUGH TV

ARTE JOHNSON WAS THE ONLY PERFORMER TO WIN AN EMMY FOR HIS WORK ON THIS COMEDY-VARIETY SERIES	**$200**	WHAT IS
NANTUCKET MEMORIAL AIRPORT DOUBLED FOR THE FICTIONAL TOM NEVERS FIELD ON THIS SITCOM	**$400**	WHAT IS
THIS ACTION SHOW STARRING RICHARD DEAN ANDERSON IS A FAVORITE OF MARGE SIMPSON'S SISTERS	**$600**	WHAT IS
THIS "MARY TYLER MOORE SHOW" SPINOFF STARRED CLORIS LEACHMAN AS THE TITLE CHARACTER	**$800**	WHAT IS
MONICA EVANS & CAROLE SHELLEY PLAYED THE PIGEON SISTERS ON THIS SITCOM, AS WELL AS IN THE STAGE & FILM VERSIONS	**$1000**	WHAT IS

DOUBLE JEOPARDY!™

TOUGH TV

$200	WHAT IS "LAUGH-IN"?	**$200**
$400	WHAT IS "WINGS"?	**$400**
$600	WHAT IS "MacGYVER"?	**$600**
$800	WHAT IS "PHYLLIS"?	**$800**
$1000	WHAT IS "THE ODD COUPLE"?	**$1000**

DOUBLE JEOPARDY!

LATIN LESSON

Clue	Value	Response
"ANNUS MIRABILIS" IS A REMARKABLE ONE OF THESE	$200	WHAT IS
ANTE BELLUM MEANS "BEFORE" THIS, SOMETHING MANY PEOPLE ARE ANTI-	$400	WHAT IS
IN "JULIUS CAESAR" SHAKESPEARE TAUGHT US THIS PHRASE MEANING "YOU ALSO"	$600	WHAT IS
BRITISH RULERS HAVE THE TITLE FIDEI DEFENSOR, MEANING THIS	$800	WHAT IS
THIS 2-WORD PHRASE REFERS TO THE PROOF A CRIME HAS BEEN COMMITTED, NOT NECESSARILY THE MURDER VICTIM	$1000	WHAT IS

DOUBLE JEOPARDY!

LATIN LESSON

$200	WHAT IS A YEAR?	**$200**
$400	WHAT IS WAR?	**$400**
$600	WHAT IS ET TU?	**$600**
$800	WHAT IS DEFENDER OF THE FAITH?	**$800**
$1000	WHAT IS CORPUS DELICTI?	**$1000**

DOUBLE JEOPARDY!

ODD WEIGHTS & MEASURES

AN EXPLOSION RATED A MEGATON IS EQUAL TO THIS MANY TONS OF TNT	**$200**	WHAT IS
A UNIT OF CLOTH MEASURE EQUAL TO 2 1/4 INCHES, OR A CARPENTER'S ITEM WHOSE SIZE IS MEASURED IN PENNIES	**$400**	WHAT IS
IN SPAIN A BRAZA WAS EQUAL TO THE REACH OF THESE OUTSTRETCHED	**$600**	WHAT ARE
YOU'RE MAKING QUITE A "PIG" OF YOURSELF CONSUMING THIS MEASURE OF LIQUID EQUAL TO 63 GALLONS	**$800**	WHAT IS
A JUDITH KRANTZ TITLE WHICH ALSO COULD BE UNITS OF APOTHECARY WEIGHT, EQUAL TO 20 GRAINS EACH	**$1000**	WHAT IS

DOUBLE JEOPARDY!

ODD WEIGHTS & MEASURES

$200   WHAT IS ONE MILLION?   **$200**

$400   WHAT IS A NAIL?   **$400**

$600   WHAT ARE THE ARMS?   **$600**

$800   WHAT IS A HOGSHEAD?   **$800**

$1000   WHAT IS "SCRUPLES"?   **$1000**

DOUBLE JEOPARDY!

A RIVER RUNS THROUGH IT

AT LONDON BRIDGE THIS RIVER IS ABOUT 800 FEET WIDE; AT ITS MOUTH, MORE THAN 5 MILES	**$200**	WHAT IS
IT'S THE ONLY MAJOR AFRICAN RIVER EMPTYING INTO THE MEDITERRANEAN SEA	**$400**	WHAT IS
THE PLATTE RIVER JOINS THE MISSOURI NEAR PLATTSMOUTH IN THIS STATE	**$600**	WHAT IS
ABOUT 60% OF THIS "MOTHER" RIVER OF RUSSIA'S WATER FLOW IS FROM SNOW; THE REST IS FROM GROUNDWATER & RAIN	**$800**	WHAT IS
COLUMBUS FIRST SIGHTED THIS VENEZUELAN RIVER IN 1498, BUT IT WASN'T EXPLORED UNTIL 33 YEARS LATER	**$1000**	WHAT IS

DOUBLE JEOPARDY!

A RIVER RUNS THROUGH IT

$200 WHAT IS THE THAMES RIVER? **$200**

$400 WHAT IS THE NILE RIVER? **$400**

$600 WHAT IS NEBRASKA? **$600**

$800 WHAT IS THE VOLGA RIVER? **$800**

$1000 WHAT IS THE ORINOCO RIVER? **$1000**

FINAL JEOPARDY!

COMPOSERS

WHEN "FANTASIA" WAS
RELEASED IN 1940, HE WAS
THE ONLY ONE OF ITS
COMPOSERS STILL ALIVE
TO HEAR HIS MUSIC

WHO IS

FINAL JEOPARDY!

COMPOSERS

WHO IS
IGOR (FYODOROVICH)
STRAVINSKY?

JEOPARDY!™

READ AMERICAN!

Clue	Value	Response
"THE CASK OF AMONTILLADO" IS AMONG HIS MACABRE MASTERPIECES	$100	WHO IS
MARK TWAIN'S TALE OF SWITCHED IDENTITIES IN TUDOR ENGLAND	$200	WHAT IS
STARTING IN 1914, HE WROTE 26 TARZAN BOOKS	$300	WHO IS
JAMES FENIMORE COOPER WROTE 5 OF THESE "TALES" NAMED FOR AN ALIAS OF NATTY BUMPPO	$400	WHAT ARE
HE COMBINED FANTASY & SATIRE IN WORKS LIKE "CAT'S CRADLE" & "GOD BLESS YOU, MR. ROSEWATER"	$500	WHO IS

JEOPARDY!™

READ AMERICAN!

$100	WHO IS EDGAR ALLAN POE?	**$100**
$200	WHAT IS "THE PRINCE AND THE PAUPER"?	**$200**
$300	WHO IS EDGAR RICE BURROUGHS?	**$300**
$400	WHAT ARE LEATHERSTOCKING TALES?	**$400**
$500	WHO IS KURT VONNEGUT (JR.)?	**$500**

JEOPARDY!

OLD YORK

Clue	Value	Response
IN 1990 YORK REINSTATED THIS AGE-OLD JOB OF CALLING THE LOCAL NEWS THROUGH THE CITY	**$100**	WHAT IS
YOU CAN'T MISS YORK MINSTER, ENGLAND'S LARGEST CHURCH IN THIS STYLE NAMED FOR A GERMANIC TRIBE	**$200**	WHAT IS
YORK IS A HUB OF THIS TYPE OF TRANSPORTATION & HAS A NATIONAL MUSEUM DEDICATED TO IT	**$300**	WHAT IS
ALAS, POOR YORK! IT WAS BURNED BY THIS NEW RULER OF ENGLAND IN THE 11th CENTURY	**$400**	WHO IS
THESE MEDIEVAL PLAYS, NONE BY AGATHA CHRISTIE, ARE PERFORMED IN A CYCLE AT YORK EVERY 4 YEARS	**$500**	WHAT ARE

JEOPARDY!™

OLD YORK

$100	WHAT IS THE TOWN CRIER?	**$100**
$200	WHAT IS GOTHIC?	**$200**
$300	WHAT IS THE RAILROAD?	**$300**
$400	WHO IS WILLIAM THE CONQUEROR? (ACCEPT: WILLIAM I)	**$400**
$500	WHAT ARE MYSTERY PLAYS?	**$500**

JEOPARDY!

HELLO, DALAI

ACCORDING TO THE DALAI LAMA'S WEB SITE, "DALAI" MEANS THIS, PRESUMABLY THE PACIFIC ONE	**$100**	WHAT IS
THE DALAI LAMA'S MOST FAMOUS DISCIPLE, THIS ACTOR PUBLISHED A BOOK OF PHOTOS OF BUDDHIST CULTURE	**$200**	WHO IS
THE DALAI LAMA IS THE SPIRITUAL REINCARNATION OF THIS ENLIGHTENED ONE, FORMERLY KNOWN AS GAUTAMA	**$300**	WHO IS
AFTER HIS EXILE IN 1959, THE DALAI LAMA WENT TO LIVE IN THE HIMALAYAN TOWN OF DHARMSALA IN THIS COUNTRY	**$400**	WHAT IS
AMONG BOOKS THE DALAI LAMA PUBLISHED IS "THE ART OF" THIS: "A HANDBOOK FOR LIVING"	**$500**	WHAT IS

JEOPARDY!™

HELLO, DALAI

$100	WHAT IS OCEAN?	**$100**
$200	WHO IS RICHARD GERE?	**$200**
$300	WHO IS BUDDHA?	**$300**
$400	WHAT IS INDIA?	**$400**
$500	WHAT IS HAPPINESS?	**$500**

JEOPARDY!

FAMILIAR PHRASES

IT'S "THE SHORTEST DISTANCE BETWEEN TWO POINTS"	**$100**	WHAT IS
IT'S WHERE SOMETHING EMBARRASSING IS SWEPT	**$200**	WHAT IS
POOL TABLE PIECE YOU DON'T WANT TO BE "BEHIND"	**$300**	WHAT IS
SHIFTING YOUR DEBTS IS "ROBBING PETER TO PAY" THIS SAINT	**$400**	WHO IS
ALEXANDER POPE CRITICIZED THOSE WHO CLAIMED TO BE AUTHORITIES WITH "FOOLS RUSH IN WHERE ANGELS" DO THIS	**$500**	WHAT IS

JEOPARDY!™

FAMILIAR PHRASES

$100	WHAT IS A STRAIGHT LINE?	**$100**
$200	WHAT IS UNDER THE RUG? (ACCEPT: UNDER THE CARPET)	**$200**
$300	WHAT IS THE EIGHT BALL?	**$300**
$400	WHO IS PAUL?	**$400**
$500	WHAT IS "FEAR TO TREAD"?	**$500**

JEOPARDY!™

CAPTAINS COURAGEOUS

IN AN EARLY ACCOUNT OF JAMESTOWN'S FIRST YEAR, HE MADE NO MENTION OF HIS RESCUE BY POCAHONTAS	**$100**	WHO IS
A CITY & ISLAND IN BRITISH COLUMBIA ARE NAMED FOR THIS SEA CAPTAIN WHO EXPLORED THE AREA IN 1792	**$200**	WHO IS
KING LOUIS XVI GAVE THIS AMERICAN REVOLUTIONARY FIGURE A GOLD SWORD & MADE HIM A CHEVALIER OF FRANCE	**$300**	WHO IS
IT TOOK HIM & HIS CREW 37 DAYS TO TRAVERSE THE SOUTH AMERICAN STRAIT NOW NAMED FOR HIM	**$400**	WHO IS
IN 1642 & 1643 THIS DUTCH CAPTAIN CIRCUMNAVIGATED AUSTRALIA WITHOUT SEEING IT	**$500**	WHO IS

JEOPARDY!

CAPTAINS COURAGEOUS

$100	WHO IS CAPTAIN JOHN SMITH?	**$100**
$200	WHO IS CAPTAIN GEORGE VANCOUVER?	**$200**
$300	WHO IS CAPTAIN JOHN PAUL JONES?	**$300**
$400	WHO IS FERDINAND MAGELLAN?	**$400**
$500	WHO IS ABEL TASMAN?	**$500**

JEOPARDY!

THE IMMORTAL ABBA

BILLBOARD CALLS THIS ABBA MORSE CODE PLEA THE "ONLY CHART HIT WHERE BOTH TITLE AND ARTIST ARE PALINDROMES"	**$100**	WHAT IS
THIS TITLE TEEN BROUGHT ABBA THEIR FIRST U.S. NO. 1 HIT	**$200**	WHO IS
1978 TITLE IN WHICH ABBA ASKED YOU TO BE A BIT OF A GAMBLER	**$300**	WHAT IS
THE 1994 FILM ABOUT THIS VEHICLE, "QUEEN OF THE DESERT" FEATURED THE MUSIC OF ABBA	**$400**	WHO IS
AGNETHA & ANNI-FRID ARE THE A'S IN THE GROUP'S NAME; BENNY & HIM ARE THE B'S	**$500**	WHO IS

JEOPARDY!

THE IMMORTAL ABBA

$100	WHAT IS "SOS"?	$100
$200	WHO IS "DANCING QUEEN"?	$200
$300	WHAT IS "TAKE A CHANCE ON ME"?	$300
$400	WHO IS PRISCILLA?	$400
$500	WHO IS BJORN (ULVAEUS)?	$500

DOUBLE JEOPARDY!

SYMPHONIES

THE "PATHETIC" SYMPHONY IS BY THIS RUSSIAN WHO ALSO GAVE US THE CELEBRATORY "1812 OVERTURE"	**$200**	WHO IS
COMPOSER CARL STALLING USED GRIEG'S "MARCH OF THE DWARFS" IN THE FIRST OF THESE DISNEY "SYMPHONIES"	**$400**	WHAT ARE
MAHLER'S MASSIVE 8th IS THE "SYMPHONY OF" THIS MANY MUSICIANS, EQUAL TO 250 QUARTETS	**$600**	WHAT IS
HAYDN'S 94th SYMPHONY IS CALLED THIS, LIKE A STARTLING TYPE OF PARTY	**$800**	WHAT IS
ONE OF THE MOVE-MENTS OF HOLST'S "THE PLANETS", OR THE NICKNAME OF MOZART'S SYMPHONY NO. 41	**$1000**	WHAT IS

DOUBLE JEOPARDY!

SYMPHONIES

$200	WHO IS PETER ILYICH TCHAIKOVSKY?	**$200**
$400	WHAT ARE SILLY SYMPHONIES?	**$400**
$600	WHAT IS 1,000?	**$600**
$800	WHAT IS SURPRISE?	**$800**
$1000	WHAT IS JUPITER?	**$1000**

DOUBLE JEOPARDY!

1948

DENMARK, NORWAY & SWEDEN COMBINED THEIR MAJOR AIRLINE COMPANIES INTO THIS ONE	**$200**	WHAT IS
ON THE THIRD BALLOT ON JUNE 24, THE REPUBLICAN NOMINATION FOR PRESIDENT WENT TO THIS GOVERNOR	**$400**	WHO IS
HE CAME INTO THE WORLD AT BUCKINGHAM PALACE ON NOVEMBER 14	**$600**	WHO IS
A YOUNG MAN NAMED NORMAN MAILER GAINED FAME WITH THIS WAR NOVEL	**$800**	WHAT IS
TO LIFE, TO LIFE, TO THIS MAN, ELECTED PROVISIONAL PRESIDENT OF ISRAEL MAY 16, 1948	**$1000**	WHO IS

DOUBLE JEOPARDY!

1948

$200	WHAT IS SAS? (ACCEPT: SCANDINAVIAN AIRLINES SYSTEM)	**$200**
$400	WHO IS THOMAS E. DEWEY?	**$400**
$600	WHO IS PRINCE CHARLES?	**$600**
$800	WHAT IS "THE NAKED AND THE DEAD"?	**$800**
$1000	WHO IS CHAIM WEIZMANN?	**$1000**

DOUBLE JEOPARDY!

HOBBIES

SOME PEOPLE RAISE BABY FOXES, CALLED THESE; SOME BUILD MODEL CARS FROM SETS OF PARTS, ALSO CALLED THESE	**$200**	WHAT ARE
TYPE OF HOBBYIST WHO KEEPS A "LIFE LIST" THAT MAY INCLUDE VIREOS & TANAGERS	**$400**	WHAT IS
IF YOU HAVEN'T TRIED THIS HOBBY WHOSE NAME INCLUDES "WORKING", YOU MAY BE A LATHE BLOOMER	**$600**	WHAT IS
THIS TYPE OF FISHING REQUIRES A "TIP-UP" DEVICE TO SIGNAL A BITE; MITTENS ARE ALSO USEFUL	**$800**	WHAT IS
IN THIS DEXTROUS HOBBY, A "CASCADE" MOVES BALLS OR PLATES IN A FIGURE 8; A "SHOWER" MOVES THEM IN A CIRCLE	**$1000**	WHAT IS

DOUBLE JEOPARDY!

HOBBIES

$200	WHAT ARE KITS?	**$200**
$400	WHAT IS A BIRDWATCHER?	**$400**
$600	WHAT IS WOODWORKING? (ACCEPT: METALWORKING)	**$600**
$800	WHAT IS ICE FISHING?	**$800**
$1000	WHAT IS JUGGLING?	**$1000**

DOUBLE JEOPARDY!

SPORTS

COMPETITION BEGAN IN 1900 FOR THIS CUP AWARDED TO A NATIONAL MEN'S TENNIS TEAM	**$200**	WHAT IS
ON SEPT. 23, 1926 THIS HEAVYWEIGHT BOXING CHAMP LOST HIS TITLE TO GENE TUNNEY IN A DECISION	**$400**	WHO IS
IN 1973 RON TURCOTTE RODE THIS HORSE TO THE FIRST TRIPLE CROWN VICTORY IN 25 YEARS	**$600**	WHAT IS
RED SOX SHORTSTOP & 1999 BATTING CHAMPION WHOSE FIRST NAME IS HIS FATHER'S, RAMON, SPELLED BACKWARDS	**$800**	WHO IS
THIS VIKINGS WIDE RECEIVER OUT OF MARSHALL HAD AN EXPLOSIVE ROOKIE YEAR IN 1998	**$1000**	WHO IS

DOUBLE JEOPARDY!

SPORTS

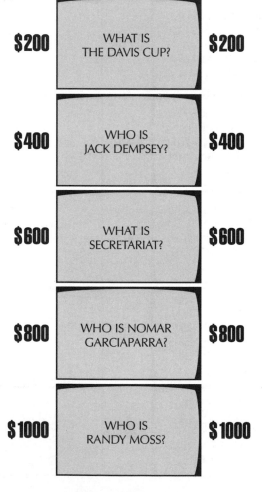

$200	WHAT IS THE DAVIS CUP?	$200
$400	WHO IS JACK DEMPSEY?	$400
$600	WHAT IS SECRETARIAT?	$600
$800	WHO IS NOMAR GARCIAPARRA?	$800
$1000	WHO IS RANDY MOSS?	$1000

DOUBLE JEOPARDY!

ITALIAN CITIES

A REGATTA HELD EACH SEPTEMBER IN THIS CITY FEATURES GONDOLA RACES ON THE GRAND CANAL	**$200**	WHAT IS
SHAKESPEARE'S FEUDING MONTAGUES & CAPULETS WERE INSPIRED BY ACTUAL INCIDENTS IN THIS CITY	**$400**	WHAT IS
THE WORLD'S MOST FAMOUS SHROUD WAS HOUSED IN THIS CITY STARTING IN 1578	**$600**	WHAT IS
THIS CITY'S PIAZZA DANTE CONTAINS THE HOUSE BELIEVED TO BE THAT OF CHRISTOPHER COLUMBUS	**$800**	WHAT IS
CONDUCTOR ARTURO TOSCANINI WAS BORN IN THIS CITY FAMOUS FOR ITS CHEESE	**$1000**	WHAT IS

DOUBLE JEOPARDY!

ITALIAN CITIES

$200	WHAT IS VENICE?	**$200**
$400	WHAT IS VERONA?	**$400**
$600	WHAT IS TURIN?	**$600**
$800	WHAT IS GENOA? (ACCEPT: GENOVA)	**$800**
$1000	WHAT IS PARMA?	**$1000**

DOUBLE JEOPARDY!

WHO SAID THAT?

THE 1758 PREFACE TO HIS "POOR RICHARD'S ALMANAC" SAYS, "HE THAT LIVES UPON HOPE WILL DIE FASTING"	**$200**	WHO IS
THE NIGHT BEFORE HIS 1968 MURDER HE SAID, "I'M NOT WORRIED ABOUT ANYTHING. I'M NOT FEARING ANY MAN"	**$400**	WHO IS
COMEDIAN WHOSE MOST FAMOUS LINE WAS "TAKE MY WIFE— PLEASE!"	**$600**	WHO IS
"I CAN RESIST EVERY-THING EXCEPT TEMPTATION", HE WROTE IN "LADY WINDERMERE'S FAN"	**$800**	WHO IS
THIS FEMINIST SAID, "SOME OF US ARE BECOMING THE MEN WE WANTED TO MARRY"	**$1000**	WHO IS

DOUBLE JEOPARDY!

WHO SAID THAT?

$200	WHO IS BENJAMIN FRANKLIN?	**$200**
$400	WHO IS MARTIN LUTHER KING JR.?	**$400**
$600	WHO IS HENNY YOUNGMAN?	**$600**
$800	WHO IS OSCAR WILDE?	**$800**
$1000	WHO IS GLORIA STEINEM?	**$1000**

FINAL JEOPARDY!

TELEVISION PERSONALITIES

HE WAS ORDAINED BY
PITTSBURGH PRESBYTERY IN
1962 WITH A CHARGE TO
WORK WITH CHILDREN
THROUGH THE MEDIA

WHO IS

FINAL JEOPARDY!

TELEVISION PERSONALITIES

WHO IS FRED ROGERS?
(ACCEPT: MISTER ROGERS)

JEOPARDY!

THE LAND OF OZ

Clue	Value	Response
THIS PAVING MATERIAL OF THE ROAD TO THE EMERALD CITY IS IN NEED OF REPAIRS	$100	WHAT IS
THE "WIZARD" OF OZ IS FROM OMAHA, NEBRASKA, NOT FAR FROM THIS STATE WHERE DOROTHY LIVES	$200	WHAT IS
AS SEEN IN CHAPTER 2, THEY'RE ABOUT AS TALL AS DOROTHY & WEAR FOOT-HIGH POINTED HATS	$300	WHAT ARE
PART OF OZ IS POPULATED BY BREAKABLE PEOPLE MADE OF THIS, ALSO THE NAME OF A REAL COUNTRY	$400	WHAT IS
IN THE BOOK, THIS EVIL PERSONAGE HAS ONLY ONE EYE & HER SLAVES ARE CALLED WINKIES	$500	WHO IS

JEOPARDY!

THE LAND OF OZ

$100 — WHAT IS YELLOW BRICK? — **$100**

$200 — WHAT IS KANSAS? — **$200**

$300 — WHAT ARE MUNCHKINS? — **$300**

$400 — WHAT IS CHINA? — **$400**

$500 — WHO IS THE WICKED WITCH OF THE WEST? — **$500**

JEOPARDY!

FORTS

Clue	Value	Response
THIS KENTUCKY FORT INCLUDES THE PATTON MUSEUM OF CAVALRY & ARMOR IN ADDITION TO ALL THAT GOLD	**$100**	WHAT IS
THIS INDIANA CITY RECONSTRUCTED ITS NAMESAKE LOG STOCKADE IN THE 1970s	**$200**	WHAT IS
FORT NECESSITY WAS BUILT BY THIS FUTURE GENERAL & IN 1754 WAS THE SITE OF HIS ONLY SURRENDER	**$300**	WHO IS
HOME OF THE XVIII AIRBORNE CORPS, THIS N.C. FORT CAN BOAST IT WAS NAMED FOR A CONFEDERATE GENERAL	**$400**	WHAT IS
THIS SEAT OF LARIMER COUNTY, COLORADO GREW UP AROUND A MILITARY OUTPOST BEGINNING IN THE 1860s	**$500**	WHAT IS

JEOPARDY!™

FORTS

$100 — WHAT IS FORT KNOX? — $100

$200 — WHAT IS FORT WAYNE? — $200

$300 — WHO IS GEORGE WASHINGTON? — $300

$400 — WHAT IS FORT BRAGG? — $400

$500 — WHAT IS FORT COLLINS? — $500

JEOPARDY!

5 GUYS NAMED MOE

LAST NAME OF MOE OF THE THREE STOOGES	**$100**	WHAT IS
MOE STRAUSS FOUNDED THIS AUTO PARTS CHAIN ALONG WITH MANNY ROSENFIELD & JACK JACKSON	**$200**	WHAT IS
MAJOR LEAGUE CATCHER MOE BERG WAS ALSO A WWII SPY FOR THIS AGENCY, PRECURSOR OF THE CIA	**$300**	WHAT IS
TERM FOR THE TYPE OF COUNTRY MUSIC MOE BANDY PLAYS, THE CLUBS WHERE HE BEGAN, OR THE "QUEEN" HE SANG OF IN 1981	**$400**	WHAT IS
THIS "KOOL" RAPPER'S ALBUM "HOW YA LIKE ME NOW" BEGAN A RIVALRY WITH LL COOL J	**$500**	WHO IS

JEOPARDY!™

5 GUYS NAMED MOE

$100 | WHAT IS HOWARD? (ACCEPT: HOROWITZ) | $100

$200 | WHAT IS PEP BOYS? (ACCEPT: PEP AUTO SUPPLIES) | $200

$300 | WHAT IS THE OSS? (ACCEPT: OFFICE OF STRATEGIC SERVICES) | $300

$400 | WHAT IS HONKY TONK? | $400

$500 | WHO IS KOOL MOE DEE? | $500

JEOPARDY!

DRESS UP

DOGGONE! THESE CLASSIC SUEDE SHOES SHARE THEIR NAME WITH A SOUTHERN CORNMEAL TREAT	**$100**	WHAT ARE
"INVENTIVE" NAME FOR LEATHER SHOES & PURSES COATED WITH VARNISH FOR A HARD GLOSSY FINISH	**$200**	WHAT IS
IT'S A MONK'S HOOD OR A DRAPED NECKLINE FOR WOMEN THAT FALLS IN SOFT FOLDS	**$300**	WHAT IS
THIS FORM-FITTING BODYSUIT FOR DANCERS & ACROBATS IS NAMED FOR A 19th CENTURY FRENCH AERIALIST	**$400**	WHAT IS
IN MEXICO THIS LARGE BLACK VEIL IS COMMONLY WORN OVER A HIGH COMB	**$500**	WHAT IS

JEOPARDY!

DRESS UP

$100 WHAT ARE HUSH PUPPIES? **$100**

$200 WHAT IS PATENT (LEATHER)? **$200**

$300 WHAT IS A COWL (NECK)? **$300**

$400 WHAT IS A LEOTARD? **$400**

$500 WHAT IS A MANTILLA? **$500**

JEOPARDY!

THEIR SECRET IDENTITIES

DON DIEGO DE LA VEGA	**$100**	WHO IS
TV's DR. DAVID BANNER	**$200**	WHO IS
THE COMICS' PETER PARKER	**$300**	WHO IS
TV's BARBARA GORDON	**$400**	WHO IS
DUMAS' EDMOND DANTES	**$500**	WHO IS

JEOPARDY!

THEIR SECRET IDENTITIES

$100	WHO IS ZORRO?	**$100**
$200	WHO IS THE (INCREDIBLE) HULK?	**$200**
$300	WHO IS SPIDER-MAN?	**$300**
$400	WHO IS BATGIRL?	**$400**
$500	WHO IS THE COUNT OF MONTE CRISTO?	**$500**

JEOPARDY!™

"TEN"SION

SHE SHARED "MUSKRAT LOVE" WITH THE CAPTAIN	**$100**	WHO IS
INFLAMMATION NAMED FOR A SPORT & A JOINT	**$200**	WHAT IS
PSYCHIATRIST DICK DIVER IS A CENTRAL CHARACTER IN THIS JAZZ AGE NOVEL	**$300**	WHAT IS
NOTABLE NEPALESE NORGAY	**$400**	WHO IS
IF YOU WANT TO PEEK AT SPAIN'S HIGHEST PEAK, LOOK FOR EL TEIDE ON THIS ISLAND	**$500**	WHAT IS

JEOPARDY!™

"TEN"SION

$100 WHO IS (TONI) TENNILLE? **$100**

$200 WHAT IS TENNIS ELBOW? **$200**

$300 WHAT IS "TENDER IS THE NIGHT"? **$300**

$400 WHO IS TENZING (NORGAY)? (ACCEPT: TENZIG) **$400**

$500 WHAT IS TENERIFE? **$500**

272

DOUBLE JEOPARDY!

THE LIBRARY OF ALEXANDRIA

Clue	Value	Response
TO MAKE UP FOR DAMAGE JULIUS CAESAR DID TO THE LIBRARY, THIS MAN GAVE CLEOPATRA 200,000 MANUSCRIPTS	**$200**	WHO IS
LIBRARIAN ZENODOTUS DIVIDED THESE 2 HOMER WORKS INTO 24 BOOKS EACH	**$400**	WHAT IS
OFTEN SEEN AROUND THE STACKS WAS THIS "ELEMENTS" AUTHOR	**$600**	WHO IS
THIRD LIBRARIAN ERATOSTHENES DETERMINED THIS MEASUREMENT OF THE EARTH VERY CLOSE TO THE ACTUAL 25,000 MILES	**$800**	WHAT IS
THE FOURTH LIBRARIAN SHARED HIS NAME WITH THIS AUTHOR OF "THE BIRDS", WHOSE WORKS HE CRITIQUED	**$1000**	WHO IS

DOUBLE JEOPARDY!

THE LIBRARY OF ALEXANDRIA

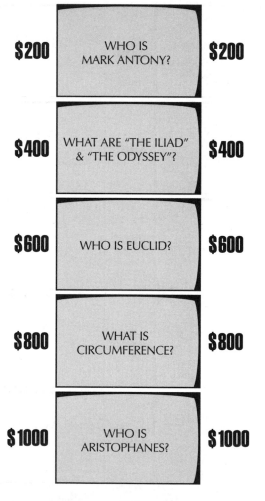

$200 — WHO IS MARK ANTONY? — **$200**

$400 — WHAT ARE "THE ILIAD" & "THE ODYSSEY"? — **$400**

$600 — WHO IS EUCLID? — **$600**

$800 — WHAT IS CIRCUMFERENCE? — **$800**

$1000 — WHO IS ARISTOPHANES? — **$1000**

DOUBLE JEOPARDY!

OPERATIC DEMISES

Clue	Value	Response
IN A BIBLICAL OPERA, THIS SHORN STRONGMAN REALLY BRINGS DOWN THE HOUSE	$200	WHO IS
A CRAP GAME ON CATFISH ROW TURNS DEADLY WHEN CROWN KILLS ROBBINS WITH A COTTON-HOOK IN THIS OPERA	$400	WHAT IS
IN A MELVILLE-INSPIRED OPERA, THIS YOUNG SAILOR IS HANGED FROM THE YARDARM OF THE H.M.S. INDOMITABLE	$600	WHO IS
IN "ELEGY FOR YOUNG LOVERS" 2 LOVERS EXPIRE WHILE SEARCHING FOR EDELWEISS IN THESE MOUNTAINS IN AUSTRIA	$800	WHAT ARE
IN A RICHARD STRAUSS OPERA, THIS DAUGHTER OF AGAMEMNON IS SO "COMPLEX" THAT SHE DANCES HERSELF TO DEATH	$1000	WHO IS

DOUBLE JEOPARDY!™

OPERATIC DEMISES

$200	WHO IS SAMSON?	**$200**
$400	WHAT IS "PORGY AND BESS"?	**$400**
$600	WHO IS BILLY BUDD?	**$600**
$800	WHAT ARE THE ALPS?	**$800**
$1000	WHO IS ELEKTRA?	**$1000**

DOUBLE JEOPARDY!

CELEBRATIONS

NOVEMBER 3 IS THE NATIONAL DAY TO CELEBRATE THIS, BE IT TUNA FISH OR PEANUT BUTTER & JELLY	**$200**	WHAT IS
CONFEDERATE HEROES DAY IS CELEBRATED JANUARY 19, THE BIRTHDAY OF THIS GENERAL	**$400**	WHO IS
APPROPRIATELY, NATIONAL STRESS AWARENESS DAY IS OBSERVED ON THIS DATE, ONE DAY AFTER "TAX DAY"	**$600**	WHAT IS
DICTIONARY DAY, OCTOBER 16, CELE-BRATES THE BIRTHDAY OF THIS AMERICAN LEXICOGRAPHER; LOOK IT UP!	**$800**	WHO IS
THIS DATE ON WHICH WWII ENDED IN EUROPE IN 1945 IS A LEGAL HOLIDAY IN FRANCE	**$1000**	WHAT IS

DOUBLE JEOPARDY!

CELEBRATIONS

$200	WHAT IS A SANDWICH?	**$200**
$400	WHO IS ROBERT E. LEE?	**$400**
$600	WHAT IS APRIL 16?	**$600**
$800	WHO IS NOAH WEBSTER?	**$800**
$1000	WHAT IS MAY 8?	**$1000**

DOUBLE JEOPARDY!

"HARD" & "EASY" MOVIES

Clue	Value	Response
I'M AWFULLY FONDA HOPPER IN THIS 1969 CLASSIC	**$200**	WHAT IS
1964 FILM THAT BROUGHT US A DAY IN THE LIFE OF THE FAB FOUR	**$400**	WHAT IS
IN THIS FILM THAT LAUNCHED A SERIES, BRUCE WILLIS BATTLES BADDIES IN AN OFFICE TOWER	**$600**	WHAT IS
BOGART'S LAST FILM, IT WAS BOUT WHAT GOES DOWN IN THE WORLD OF PRIZEFIGHTING	**$800**	WHAT IS
NEW ORLEANS DETECTIVE DENNIS QUAID CROSSES SWORDS WITH & FALLS FOR D.A. ELLEN BARKIN IN IT	**$1000**	WHAT IS

DOUBLE JEOPARDY!

"HARD" & "EASY" MOVIES

$200	WHAT IS "EASY RIDER"?	$200
$400	WHAT IS "A HARD DAY'S NIGHT"?	$400
$600	WHAT IS "DIE HARD"?	$600
$800	WHAT IS "THE HARDER THEY FALL"?	$800
$1000	WHAT IS "THE BIG EASY"?	$1000

DOUBLE JEOPARDY!

ASSASSINATIONS

THIS U.S. PRESIDENT DIED OF A GUNSHOT WOUND IN SEPTEMBER 1881	**$200**	WHO IS
EXECUTED IN 1918, THIS CZAR HAS SINCE BEEN MADE A SAINT BY THE RUSSIAN ORTHODOX CHURCH ABROAD	**$400**	WHO IS
U.S. FLAGS FLEW AT HALF STAFF AFTER THIS ISRAELI PRIME MINISTER WAS SLAIN IN 1995	**$600**	WHO IS
1980s VICTIMS OF BOMBS IN THIS CITY INCLUDED PRESIDENT-ELECT BASHIR GEMAYEL & HUNDREDS OF U.S. MARINES	**$800**	WHAT IS
A PRAETORIAN GUARD HAD ENOUGH OF THIS INSANE ROMAN EMPEROR & MURDERED HIM IN 41 A.D.	**$1000**	WHO IS

DOUBLE JEOPARDY!

ASSASSINATIONS

$200 — WHO IS JAMES A. GARFIELD? — $200

$400 — WHO IS NICHOLAS II? — $400

$600 — WHO IS YITZHAK RABIN? — $600

$800 — WHAT IS BEIRUT? — $800

$1000 — WHO IS CALIGULA? — $1000

DOUBLE JEOPARDY!

12-LETTER WORDS

BRITANNICA OR WORLD BOOK, FOR EXAMPLE	**$200**	WHAT IS
IT'S A DOCTOR WHOSE SPECIALTY IS OPERATING ON THE BRAIN & SPINAL CORD	**$400**	WHAT IS
IN BOXING, IT'S THE WEIGHT CLASS BETWEEN LIGHTWEIGHT & MIDDLEWEIGHT	**$600**	WHAT IS
HOW JIM LANGE USED TO REFER TO A FEMALE CONTESTANT ON TV'S "THE DATING GAME"	**$800**	WHAT IS
FROM THE LATIN FOR "TO WALK", IT'S ANOTHER TERM FOR A BABY BUGGY, ESPECIALLY IN BRITAIN	**$1000**	WHAT IS

DOUBLE JEOPARDY!

12-LETTER WORDS

$200	WHAT IS ENCYCLOPEDIA?	**$200**
$400	WHAT IS A NEUROSURGEON?	**$400**
$600	WHAT IS WELTERWEIGHT?	**$600**
$800	WHAT IS BACHELORETTE?	**$800**
$1000	WHAT IS PERAMBULATOR?	**$1000**

FINAL JEOPARDY!

LATIN PHRASES

IT CAN REFER TO THE HOST
USED IN THE EUCHARIST, OR
A CITY SOUTHWEST OF
HOUSTON

WHAT IS

FINAL JEOPARDY!

LATIN PHRASES

WHAT IS CORPUS CHRISTI?

JEOPARDY!

AROUND THE WORLD

IT WASN'T UNTIL 1954, THE YEAR AFTER IT WAS FIRST SCALED, THAT A SURVEY SET IT AT 29,028 FEET	**$100**	WHAT IS
SMALL SHIPS CAN TRAVEL FROM THIS RIVER'S MOUTH 2,300 MILES UPSTREAM TO IQUITOS, PERU	**$200**	WHAT IS
IT'S 8 STORIES HIGH, CYLINDRICAL IN SHAPE & ABOUT 14 FEET OFF THE PERPENDICULAR	**$300**	WHAT IS
ANYTHING BUT BORING ARE THE NORTHERN LIGHTS, ALSO KNOWN BY THIS LATIN NAME	**$400**	WHAT IS
THIS NATURAL WONDER EXTENDS 1,250 MILES OFF THE NORTHEASTERN COAST OF AUSTRALIA	**$500**	WHAT IS

JEOPARDY!™

AROUND THE WORLD

$100	WHAT IS MOUNT EVEREST?	**$100**
$200	WHAT IS THE AMAZON?	**$200**
$300	WHAT IS THE LEANING TOWER OF PISA?	**$300**
$400	WHAT IS AURORA BOREALIS?	**$400**
$500	WHAT IS THE GREAT BARRIER REEF?	**$500**

JEOPARDY!

QUOTABLE POTENT POTABLES

Clue	Value	Response
IN GERMANY THESE PARTY ESSENTIALS ARE CALLED "WEIN, WEIB UND GESANG"	**$100**	WHAT ARE
IT'S THE COCKTAIL THAT JAMES BOND LIKES "SHAKEN, NOT STIRRED"	**$200**	WHAT IS
THIS ACTOR DRAWLED, "SOME WEASEL TOOK THE CORK OUT OF MY LUNCH"	**$300**	WHO IS
IN "TOM BROWN'S SCHOOL DAYS" WE READ THAT "LIFE ISN'T ALL" THIS "AND SKITTLES"	**$400**	WHAT IS
SAMUEL JOHNSON SAID, "HE WHO ASPIRES TO BE A HERO MUST DRINK" THIS LIQUOR (NOT NECESSARILY COGNAC)	**$500**	WHAT IS

JEOPARDY!

QUOTABLE POTENT POTABLES

$100   WHAT ARE WINE, WOMEN & SONG?   **$100**

$200   WHAT IS A (VODKA) MARTINI?   **$200**

$300   WHO IS W.C. FIELDS?   **$300**

$400   WHAT IS BEER?   **$400**

$500   WHAT IS BRANDY?   **$500**

JEOPARDY!

MEN OF LETTERS

THIS RECLUSIVE AUTHOR'S INITIALS STAND FOR JEROME DAVID	$100	WHO IS
HIS INITIALS STAND FOR EDWARD ESTLIN— OR SHOULD IT BE edward estlin	$200	WHO IS
DAVID HERBERT WERE THE GIVEN NAMES OF THIS COAL MINER'S SON	$300	WHO IS
YOU'D USE YOUR INITIALS TOO IF YOUR NAME WAS WYSTAN HUGH, LIKE THIS POET'S	$400	WHO IS
THE WORK OF THIS MAN CHRISTENED JOHN RONALD REUEL CAN BE HOBBIT FORMING	$500	WHO IS

JEOPARDY!™

MEN OF LETTERS

$100	WHO IS J.D. SALINGER?	$100
$200	WHO IS e.e. cummings?	$200
$300	WHO IS D.H. LAWRENCE?	$300
$400	WHO IS W.H. AUDEN?	$400
$500	WHO IS J.R.R. TOLKIEN?	$500

JEOPARDY!

AFLOAT

IF YOU OFTEN CONFUSE LEFT & RIGHT, YOU'LL PROBABLY CONFUSE PORT & THIS	**$100**	WHAT IS
SOMEONE HAS TO SWAB THESE, THE EQUIVALENT OF FLOORS, INCLUDING THE POOP & ORLOP	**$200**	WHAT ARE
TO "WEIGH" THIS ISN'T TO FIND OUT HOW HEAVY IT IS, BUT TO RAISE IT SO THE SHIP CAN GET UNDER WAY	**$300**	WHAT IS
THE AFT PART OF A BOAT, OR AN ADJECTIVE FOR AN ANGRY LOOK	**$400**	WHAT IS
IN ANCIENT TIMES IT WAS A VESSEL PROPELLED BY SERVILE OARSMEN; TODAY IT'S A VESSEL'S KITCHEN	**$500**	WHAT IS

JEOPARDY!

AFLOAT

$100	WHAT IS STARBOARD?	**$100**
$200	WHAT ARE DECKS?	**$200**
$300	WHAT IS AN ANCHOR?	**$300**
$400	WHAT IS STERN?	**$400**
$500	WHAT IS THE GALLEY?	**$500**

JEOPARDY!

TV ON TV

"F.Y.I." WAS THE FICTIONAL NEWS SHOW ON THIS SITCOM	**$100**	WHAT IS
THIS "SIMPSONS" TV CLOWN HAS WORKED WITH SIDESHOW BOB, SIDESHOW MEL & SIDESHOW LUKE PERRY	**$200**	WHO IS
IT'S THE NAME OF THE HOME IMPROVEMENT SHOW FEATURED ON "HOME IMPROVEMENT"	**$300**	WHAT IS
HE PLAYED TALK SHOW HOST LARRY SANDERS ON HBO's "THE LARRY SANDERS SHOW"	**$400**	WHO IS
SHOW FEATURING PETER KRAUSE, JOSH CHARLES & FELICITY HUFFMAN AS EMPLOYEES OF THE CSC NETWORK	**$500**	WHAT IS

JEOPARDY!

TV ON TV

$100 — WHAT IS "MURPHY BROWN"? — **$100**

$200 — WHO IS KRUSTY (THE CLOWN)? (ACCEPT: HERSHEL KRUSTOFSKY) — **$200**

$300 — WHAT IS "TOOL TIME"? — **$300**

$400 — WHO IS GARRY SHANDLING? — **$400**

$500 — WHAT IS "SPORTS NIGHT"? — **$500**

JEOPARDY!™

FAMOUS BEARDS

ACCORDING TO CLEMENT CLARKE MOORE, "THE BEARD ON HIS CHIN WAS AS WHITE AS THE SNOW"	**$100**	WHO IS
IN THE 1850s HE EXHIBITED MADAME JOSEPHINE FORTUNE CLOFULLIA AS THE "BEARDED LADY FROM SWITZERLAND"	**$200**	WHO IS
END-OF-THE- ALPHABET BAND WITH DRUMMER FRANK BEARD AS THE ONLY BEARDLESS MEMBER	**$300**	WHAT IS
GRACE BEDELL, AGE 11, THOUGHT THIS MAN WOULD WIN AN ELEC-TION BY MORE THAN A HAIR IF HE GREW WHISKERS; HE AGREED	**$400**	WHO IS
FOR THIS AUSTRIAN PSYCHOANALYST, SOMETIMES A BEARD WAS JUST A BEARD	**$500**	WHO IS

JEOPARDY!

FAMOUS BEARDS

$100   WHO IS ST. NICHOLAS? (ACCEPT: ST. NICK, SANTA CLAUS)   **$100**

$200   WHO IS P(HINEAS) T(AYLOR) BARNUM?   **$200**

$300   WHAT IS ZZ TOP?   **$300**

$400   WHO IS ABRAHAM LINCOLN?   **$400**

$500   WHO IS SIGMUND FREUD?   **$500**

DOUBLE JEOPARDY!

WORLD LEADERS

Clue	Value	Response
IN NOVEMBER 1999 CHERIE, THE WIFE OF THIS BRITISH PRIME MINISTER, ANNOUNCED SHE WAS PREGNANT	**$200**	WHO IS
IN 1967 MUDA HASSANAL BOLKIAH BECAME THE INSANELY WEALTHY SULTAN OF THIS COUNTRY	**$400**	WHAT IS
HELMUT KOHL PASSED THIS MAN'S RECORD AS THE LONGEST-SERVING CHANCELLOR OF POST-WWII GERMANY	**$600**	WHO IS
PRESIDENTS OF THIS COUNTRY SINCE ITS 1970s REVOLUTION INCLUDE RAFSANJANI & KHATAMI	**$800**	WHAT IS
THIS MAN OF JAPANESE DESCENT GAINED THE PRESIDENCY OF PERU IN 1990	**$1000**	WHO IS

DOUBLE JEOPARDY!

WORLD LEADERS

$200   WHO IS TONY BLAIR? $200

$400   WHAT IS BRUNEI? $400

$600   WHO IS KONRAD ADENAUER? $600

$800   WHAT IS IRAN? $800

$1000   WHO IS ALBERTO KENYO FUJIMORI? $1000

DOUBLE JEOPARDY!

ASTRONOMY

Clue	Value	Response
THE CRAB NEBULA, FIRST OBSERVED IN 1054 A.D., CAN BE FOUND IN THIS CONSTELLATION, & THAT'S NO BULL	**$200**	WHAT IS
DUE TO ITS COILED ARMS, THE MILKY WAY IS CLASSIFIED AS THIS TYPE OF GALAXY, ALSO THE NAME OF A TYPE OF STAIRCASE	**$400**	WHAT IS
UNTIL 1974, THE 200-INCH HALE TELESCOPE ON THIS CALIFORNIA MOUNTAIN WAS THE WORLD'S LARGEST REFLECTOR	**$600**	WHAT IS
THIS ITALIAN SPENT HIS LAST 8 YEARS UNDER HOUSE ARREST FOR TEACHING...SHH! THE EARTH GOES AROUND THE SUN!	**$800**	WHO IS
BY THE TIME THIS FLOW OF GASES FROM THE SUN REACHES EARTH, ITS SPEED MAY BE 1-2 MILLION MPH	**$1000**	WHAT IS

DOUBLE JEOPARDY!

ASTRONOMY

$200 — WHAT IS TAURUS? — $200

$400 — WHAT IS A SPIRAL GALAXY? — $400

$600 — WHAT IS MOUNT PALOMAR? — $600

$800 — WHO IS GALILEO (GALILEI)? — $800

$1000 — WHAT IS THE SOLAR WIND? — $1000

DOUBLE JEOPARDY!

MOVIE STARS

YOU MAY CALL HIM ROCKY OR RAMBO, BUT HIS FRIENDS CALL HIM SLY	**$200**	WHO IS
ELSA LANCHESTER PLAYED THIS TITLE "BRIDE" WHO HAD THE WORST BAD HAIR DAY OF ALL TIME	**$400**	WHO IS
THIS STAR OF "GIRL, INTERRUPTED" IS THE GODDAUGHTER OF '60s GURU DR. TIMOTHY LEARY	**$600**	WHO IS
JAMIE LEE CURTIS WASN'T BORN YET WHEN THESE ACTORS, HER PARENTS, CO-STARRED IN "HOUDINI" IN 1953	**$800**	WHO ARE
HER FIERY PERFORMANCE AS NICK NOLTE'S DAUGHTER IN "CAPE FEAR" EARNED HER AN OSCAR NOMINATION	**$1000**	WHO IS

DOUBLE JEOPARDY!

MOVIE STARS

$200 — WHO IS SYLVESTER STALLONE? — $200

$400 — WHO IS THE BRIDE OF FRANKENSTEIN? — $400

$600 — WHO IS WINONA RYDER? — $600

$800 — WHO ARE TONY CURTIS & JANET LEIGH? — $800

$1000 — WHO IS JULIETTE LEWIS? — $1000

DOUBLE JEOPARDY!

HOT STUFF

BLACKSMITHS WERE THE ORIGINAL OPPORTUNISTS WHO "STRUCK WHILE" THIS WAS HOT	**$200**	WHAT IS
15 SECONDS AT 160 DEGREES F. KILLS THIS BACTERIUM THAT IN 1997 CAUSED THE USA's BIGGEST BEEF RECALL	**$400**	WHAT IS
A SECOND AFTER THIS HYPOTHESIZED EXPLOSION, THE TEMPERATURE WAS 10 BILLION DEGREES KELVIN	**$600**	WHAT IS
PLAIN OLD WATER IS A COMMON COOLANT FOR THIS PART OF A NUCLEAR REACTOR YOU MIGHT CALL THE "FISSION HOLE"	**$800**	WHAT IS
FORECASTS ON THIS PLANET CALL FOR HIGHS OF 800 DEGREES F. & BLACK SKIES DUE TO LACK OF SIGNIFI-CANT ATMOSPHERE	**$1000**	WHAT IS

DOUBLE JEOPARDY!

HOT STUFF

$200	WHAT IS THE IRON?	**$200**
$400	WHAT IS E. COLI (0157.H7)? (ACCEPT: ESCHERICHIA)	**$400**
$600	WHAT IS THE BIG BANG?	**$600**
$800	WHAT IS THE CORE?	**$800**
$1000	WHAT IS MERCURY?	**$1000**

DOUBLE JEOPARDY!

A CAPITAL IDEA

Clue	Value	Response
THIS CITY'S PEACE TOWER HOUSES A MEMORIAL CHAMBER COMMEMORATING CANADA'S WAR DEAD	$200	WHAT IS
THE BEAR IS THE HERALDIC SYMBOL OF THIS SWISS CAPITAL	$400	WHAT IS
THIS COUNTRY'S CAPITAL, AMMAN, LIES A BIT NORTHEAST OF THE DEAD SEA	$600	WHAT IS
THE GREEKS CALL CYPRUS' CAPITAL LEVKOSIA; THE TURKS CALL IT LEFKOSA; WE CALL IT THIS	$800	WHAT IS
ST. STEPHEN LENT A HAND, HIS MUMMIFIED RIGHT HAND, TO ST. STEPHEN'S BASILICA IN THIS CAPITAL	$1000	WHAT IS

DOUBLE JEOPARDY!

A CAPITAL IDEA

$200	WHAT IS OTTAWA? **$200**
$400	WHAT IS BERN? **$400**
$600	WHAT IS JORDAN? **$600**
$800	WHAT IS NICOSIA? **$800**
$1000	WHAT IS BUDAPEST? **$1000**

DOUBLE JEOPARDY!

"BOO"!

IT'S A FOLLOW-UP DOSE OF A VACCINE; ONE SHOULD BE GIVEN AT AGE 2 & ANOTHER BEFORE ENTERING SCHOOL	**$200**	WHAT IS
COUNT CHOCULA'S GHOSTLY COMPANION IN THE CEREAL WORLD	**$400**	WHO IS
JEM & SCOUT'S CREEPY BUT HELPFUL NEIGHBOR IN "TO KILL A MOCKINGBIRD"	**$600**	WHO IS
NICKNAME OF EYE-CATCHING P-FUNK BASSIST WILLIAM COLLINS	**$800**	WHAT IS
THIS TYPE OF ALGEBRA USES "AND", "OR" & "NOT" AS OPERATORS THAT RESTRICT SEARCHES ON THE INTERNET	**$1000**	WHAT IS

DOUBLE JEOPARDY!™

"BOO"!

$200 — WHAT IS A BOOSTER SHOT? — **$200**

$400 — WHO IS BOO BERRY? — **$400**

$600 — WHO IS (ARTHUR) BOO RADLEY? — **$600**

$800 — WHAT IS BOOTSY? — **$800**

$1000 — WHAT IS BOOLEAN? — **$1000**

FINAL JEOPARDY!

RETAIL

FRUSTRATED BY
DEPARTMENT STORES,
DONALD FISHER FOUNDED
THIS CHAIN IN 1969 AS A
RECORD & JEANS STORE

WHAT IS

FINAL JEOPARDY!

RETAIL

WHAT IS THE GAP (, INC.)?

JEOPARDY!™

What Is Quiz Book 2?

JEOPARDY!

AMERICAN LITERATURE

"THE COLOR PURPLE" IS THE BEST-KNOWN WORK BY THIS GEORGIA-BORN WOMAN	**$100**	WHO IS
TO RESEARCH "AIRPORT", HE SPENT HOURS IN AIRPORTS ABSORBING THE ATMOSPHERE	**$200**	WHO IS
HEMINGWAY TOOK THE TITLE OF THIS NOVEL ABOUT JOURNALIST JAKE BARNES FROM A PASSAGE IN ECCLESIASTES	**$300**	WHAT IS
"NATURE", AN 1836 ESSAY BY THIS TRANSCENDENTALIST & FRIEND OF THOREAU, WAS PUBLISHED ANONYMOUSLY	**$400**	WHO IS
IN CHAPTER 2 OF "TOM SAWYER", TOM CONS OTHER BOYS INTO HELPING HIM WITH THIS TASK	**$500**	WHAT IS

1

JEOPARDY!

AMERICAN LITERATURE

$100

WHO IS
ALICE WALKER?

$100

$200

WHO IS
ARTHUR HAILEY?

$200

$300

WHAT IS
"THE SUN ALSO RISES"?

$300

$400

WHO IS RALPH
WALDO EMERSON?

$400

$500

WHAT IS
WHITEWASHING
A FENCE?

$500

JEOPARDY!™

BIBLICAL HOTTIES

DURING GOD'S FIRST CONVERSATION WITH MOSES, IT WAS ON FIRE BUT "WAS NOT CONSUMED"	**$100**	WHAT IS
ANGELS HAD TO DRAG LOT & HIS FAMILY OUT OF THIS CITY BEFORE THINGS GOT TOO HOT	**$200**	WHAT IS
IT WAS HEATED 7 TIMES HOTTER THAN NORMAL FOR SHADRACH, MESHACH & ABEDNEGO	**$300**	WHAT IS
THIS VEHICLE "OF FIRE" ON WHICH ELIJAH ASCENDED INTO HEAVEN WAS A REAL "HOT ROD"	**$400**	WHAT IS
ON THIS HOLY DAY, TONGUES OF FIRE APPEARED TO THE APOSTLES, WHO THEN BEGAN TO SPEAK IN TONGUES	**$500**	WHAT IS

JEOPARDY!™

BIBLICAL HOTTIES

$100	WHAT IS THE BURNING BUSH?	**$100**
$200	WHAT IS SODOM?	**$200**
$300	WHAT IS THE (FIERY) FURNACE?	**$300**
$400	WHAT IS THE CHARIOT (OF FIRE)?	**$400**
$500	WHAT IS PENTECOST?	**$500**

JEOPARDY!™

JOHN HUGHES FILMS

Clue	Value	Response
IT'S THE 1990 STORY OF AN 8-YEAR-OLD BOY ACCIDENTALLY ABANDONED AT CHRISTMAS	**$100**	WHAT IS
TITLE CHARACTER WHO SAYS, "THIS IS MY NINTH SICK DAY THIS SEMESTER . . . SO I BETTER MAKE THIS ONE COUNT"	**$200**	WHO IS
MOLLY RINGWALD'S FAMILY FORGETS HER BIRTHDAY WHILE PREPARING FOR HER SISTER'S WEDDING IN THIS FILM	**$300**	WHAT IS
STEVE MARTIN & JOHN CANDY USE THESE TITLE MODES OF TRANSPORTATION TO TRY TO GET HOME FOR THANKSGIVING	**$400**	WHAT ARE
HE PLAYED THE BRAINY BRIAN IN "THE BREAKFAST CLUB"	**$500**	WHO IS

JEOPARDY!™

JOHN HUGHES FILMS

$100	WHAT IS "HOME ALONE"?	**$100**
$200	WHO IS FERRIS BUELLER?	**$200**
$300	WHAT IS "SIXTEEN CANDLES"?	**$300**
$400	WHAT ARE "PLANES, TRAINS & AUTOMOBILES"?	**$400**
$500	WHO IS ANTHONY MICHAEL HALL?	**$500**

JEOPARDY!™

COUGH, COUGH

COMMON NAME OF PERTUSSIS	**$100**	WHAT IS
THESE BROTHERS STARTED SELLING THEIR COUGH DROPS IN 1847	**$200**	WHO ARE
A SHORT, DRY COUGH, OR A TRITE WRITER FOR HIRE	**$300**	WHAT IS
THE MEN'S MALADY A DOCTOR IS USUALLY CHECKING FOR AFTER HE ASKS THE PATIENT TO "TURN YOUR HEAD AND COUGH"	**$400**	WHAT IS
THIS COUGH SUPPRESSANT IS AN OPIUM DERIVATIVE	**$500**	WHAT IS

JEOPARDY!™

COUGH, COUGH

$100   WHAT IS WHOOPING COUGH? $100

$200   WHO ARE THE SMITH BROTHERS? $200

$300   WHAT IS A HACK? $300

$400   WHAT IS A HERNIA? $400

$500   WHAT IS CODEINE? $500

JEOPARDY!™

LET'S CROSS THAT BRIDGE

BEFORE ITS COMPLETION IN 1917, THE QUEBEC RAILWAY BRIDGE OVER THIS RIVER COLLAPSED TWICE	**$100**	WHAT IS
CLEVELANDER HART CRANE'S POEM "THE BRIDGE" PRAISES THIS ONE ACROSS NYC's EAST RIVER	**$200**	WHAT IS
THIS TYPE OF MOVABLE BRIDGE THAT PROTECTED CASTLES IS ALSO USED TO PERMIT RIVER TRAFFIC	**$300**	WHAT IS
RIVER CROSSED BY THE ALLENBY, OR KING HUSSEIN, BRIDGE	**$400**	WHAT IS
PUENTE DE PIEDRAS IS A CENTURIES-OLD BRIDGE IN THIS COUNTRY WHERE "THE BRIDGE OF SAN LUIS REY" IS SET	**$500**	WHAT IS

JEOPARDY!™

LET'S CROSS THAT BRIDGE

$100	WHAT IS THE ST. LAWRENCE RIVER?	$100
$200	WHAT IS THE BROOKLYN BRIDGE?	$200
$300	WHAT IS A DRAWBRIDGE? (ACCEPT: BASCULE)	$300
$400	WHAT IS THE JORDAN?	$400
$500	WHAT IS PERU?	$500

JEOPARDY!

WHEN WE COME TO "_IT_"

A CATCHER'S CATCHER	**$100**	WHAT IS
"QUICK" ONES ARE FAST WITH A JOKE; "HALF" ONES DON'T GET THE JOKE	**$200**	WHAT ARE
ON TV, YOU CAN FIND "CAROLINE IN" IT	**$300**	WHAT IS
YOU WON'T FIND "CAROLINE IN" THIS MEDIUM-SIZED ITALIAN TUBULAR PASTA	**$400**	WHAT IS
SOMETHING MOVING IN IRREGULAR BURSTS GOES IN THESE "AND STARTS"	**$500**	WHAT ARE

JEOPARDY!™

WHEN WE COME TO "_IT_"

$100   WHAT IS A MITT? $100

$200   WHAT ARE WITS? $200

$300   WHAT IS THE CITY? $300

$400   WHAT IS ZITI? $400

$500   WHAT ARE FITS? $500

DOUBLE JEOPARDY!

BUCHANAN . . . JAMES BUCHANAN

A GOOD FRIEND OF BUCHANAN'S WAS THIS MAN WHO WENT ON TO BE PRESIDENT—OF THE CONFEDERACY	**$200**	WHO IS
BUCHANAN WAS BORN IN THE TOWN OF STONY BATTER IN THIS STATE; HE DIED & WAS BURIED IN LANCASTER THERE	**$400**	WHAT IS
BUCHANAN WAS ON BOTH SIDES OF THE FENCE FOR THIS NUMERICAL BOUNDARY OF OREGON THAT POLK WANTED	**$600**	WHAT IS
IN THE 1856 ELECTION, BUCHANAN BEAT THIS FORMER PRESIDENT WHO RAN AS A KNOW-NOTHING	**$800**	WHO IS
BUCHANAN DIDN'T LIKE THIS ILLINOIS "LITTLE GIANT" THOUGH HE MAY HAVE GIVEN MONEY TO BUCHAN-AN'S CAMPAIGN	**$1000**	WHO IS

13

DOUBLE JEOPARDY!

BUCHANAN . . . JAMES BUCHANAN

$200 — WHO IS JEFFERSON DAVIS? — $200

$400 — WHAT IS PENNSYLVANIA? — $400

$600 — WHAT IS "FIFTY-FOUR FORTY"? — $600

$800 — WHO IS MILLARD FILLMORE? — $800

$1000 — WHO IS STEPHEN DOUGLAS? — $1000

DOUBLE JEOPARDY!

JAZZ NICKNAMES

HE WAS KNOWN AS POPS AS WELL AS SATCHMO	**$200**	WHO IS
WITH THIS NICKNAME, JULIAN EDWIN ADDERLY BARRELLED DOWN "THEM DIRTY BLUES"	**$400**	WHAT IS
ORAN PAGE, TRUMPETER & ACCOMPANIST TO BESSIE SMITH, WAS KNOWN AS THIS, LIKE A "M*A*S*H" CHARACTER	**$600**	WHAT IS
HE GAINED FAME AS THE "HI DE HO" MAN	**$800**	WHO IS
THAT HE WAS BORN AS AN ARMANDO IN 1941 SHOULD TELL YOU THIS "CHICK" IS A GUY	**$1000**	WHO IS

DOUBLE JEOPARDY!

JAZZ NICKNAMES

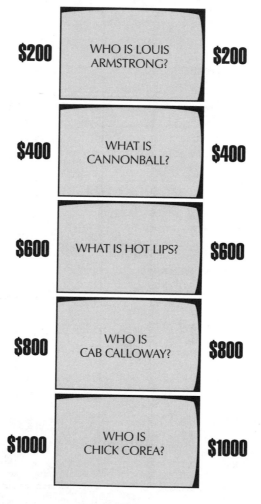

$200   WHO IS LOUIS ARMSTRONG? $200

$400   WHAT IS CANNONBALL? $400

$600   WHAT IS HOT LIPS? $600

$800   WHO IS CAB CALLOWAY? $800

$1000   WHO IS CHICK COREA? $1000

DOUBLE JEOPARDY!

BUSINESS FOUNDERS

IN THE 19th C. HE FLED THE GERMAN MILITARY DRAFT & WENT ON TO BREW BEER IN GOLDEN, COLORADO	**$200**	WHO IS
TODD McFARLANE'S CAREER DRAWING SPIDERMAN FOR THIS COMICS LINE SPAWNED HIS OWN PRIVATE COMPANY	**$400**	WHAT IS
IN 1968 ROBERT NOYCE & GORDON MOORE FOUNDED THIS MICRO-CHIP COMPANY & SOON BROUGHT ANDREW GROVE ON BOARD	**$600**	WHAT IS
THE COMPANY FOUNDED BY THIS MAN IN 1876 DEVELOPED INSULIN, MANY ANTIBIOTICS & PROZAC	**$800**	WHO IS
"UNCLE HERB" KELLEHER FOUNDED THIS NO-FRILLS AIRLINE NAMED FOR A QUADRANT OF THE U.S.	**$1000**	WHAT IS

DOUBLE JEOPARDY!

BUSINESS FOUNDERS

$200	WHO IS ADOLPH COORS?	$200
$400	WHAT IS MARVEL?	$400
$600	WHAT IS INTEL? (ACCEPT: INTEGRATED ELECTRONICS)	$600
$800	WHO IS (COLONEL) ELI LILLY?	$800
$1000	WHAT IS SOUTHWEST AIRLINES?	$1000

DOUBLE JEOPARDY!

THE COMICS

TESS TRUEHEART IS THE SWEETHEART OF THIS POLICE DETECTIVE DRAWN BY CHESTER GOULD	**$200**	WHO IS
ON JANUARY 1, 1995 "THE FAR SIDE" ENDED; ON DECEMBER 31, 1995 THIS BILL WATTERSON STRIP DID, TOO	**$400**	WHAT IS
BRENDA STARR'S LONGTIME JOB	**$600**	WHAT IS
IN THE STRIP "CROCK", QUENCH IS ONE OF THESE ANIMALS	**$800**	WHAT IS
"UNCLEAR ON THE CONCEPT" IS A COMMON THEME IN THIS JOE MARTIN STRIP	**$1000**	WHAT IS

DOUBLE JEOPARDY!™

THE COMICS

$200	WHO IS DICK TRACY?	$200
$400	WHAT IS "CALVIN & HOBBES"?	$400
$600	WHAT IS REPORTER?	$600
$800	WHAT IS A CAMEL?	$800
$1000	WHAT IS "MR. BOFFO"?	$1000

DOUBLE JEOPARDY!

CHEM LAB

GLENN SEABORG, A DISCOVERER OF THIS DEADLY ELEMENT, SAID IT WAS GIVEN THE SYMBOL Pu "AS A JOKE"	**$200**	WHAT IS
GASOLINE IS MADE UP OF HUNDREDS OF THESE, THE SIMPLEST ORGANIC COMPOUNDS	**$400**	WHAT ARE
IT'S DEFINED AS THE CHEMISTRY OF SUBSTANCES THAT LACK CARBON BONDS	**$600**	WHAT IS
THIS COLORLESS GAS IS THE VC IN PVC	**$800**	WHAT IS
THE GREEK PREFIX MEANING "EQUAL" IS USED IN THIS TERM FOR 2 FORMS OF THE SAME ELEMENT	**$1000**	WHAT IS

DOUBLE JEOPARDY!

CHEM LAB

$200 WHAT IS PLUTONIUM? $200

$400 WHAT ARE HYDROCARBONS? $400

$600 WHAT IS INORGANIC CHEMISTRY? $600

$800 WHAT IS VINYL CHLORIDE? $800

$1000 WHAT IS ISOTOPE? $1000

DOUBLE JEOPARDY!

GIMME AN "F"

A TYPE OF UNDER-THE-TABLE FLIRTING IS CALLED "PLAYING" THIS	**$200**	WHAT IS
SHARK PART THAT'S SLANG FOR A 5-DOLLAR BILL	**$400**	WHAT IS
THE U.S.S. CONSTITUTION IS ONE OF THE MOST FAMOUS OF THESE SAILING SHIPS	**$600**	WHAT ARE
THOMAS GRAY WROTE, "WHERE IGNORANCE IS BLISS, 'TIS" THIS "TO BE WISE"	**$800**	WHAT IS
SOME CALL THIS ISLAND COUNTRY THE "CROSSROADS OF THE SOUTH PACIFIC"	**$1000**	WHAT IS

DOUBLE JEOPARDY!

GIMME AN "F"

$200   WHAT IS FOOTSIE(S)? $200

$400   WHAT IS A FIN? $400

$600   WHAT ARE FRIGATES? $600

$800   WHAT IS "FOLLY"? $800

$1000   WHAT IS FIJI? $1000

FINAL JEOPARDY!

HAMLET

THE GRAVEDIGGER SAYS
HAMLET WAS SENT TO THIS
COUNTRY BECAUSE "THERE
THE MEN ARE AS MAD AS HE"

WHAT IS

FINAL JEOPARDY!

HAMLET

WHAT IS ENGLAND?

JEOPARDY!

THE BIG APPLE

SHEEP MEADOW & THE TURTLE POND CAN BE FOUND IN THIS 843-ACRE PUBLIC PLAYGROUND	**$100**	WHAT IS
ONE WORLD TRADE CENTER IS THE TALLEST BUILDING IN THE CITY; THIS IS THE SECOND TALLEST	**$200**	WHAT IS
A MAST TO MOOR DIRIGIBLES WAS ADDED TO THIS SKYSCRAPER, BUT ONLY ONE EVER MOORED SUCCESSFULLY	**$300**	WHAT IS
HE WAS INAUGURATED FOR HIS SECOND TIME AS MAYOR OF NEW YORK CITY JANUARY 1, 1998	**$400**	WHO IS
THERE'S A STATUE OF THIS "YANKEE DOODLE DANDY" "OVER THERE" IN TIMES SQUARE	**$500**	WHO IS

JEOPARDY!™

THE BIG APPLE

$100 — WHAT IS CENTRAL PARK? — $100

$200 — WHAT IS TWO WORLD TRADE CENTER? — $200

$300 — WHAT IS THE EMPIRE STATE BUILDING? — $300

$400 — WHO IS RUDOLPH W. GIULIANI? — $400

$500 — WHO IS GEORGE M. COHAN? — $500

JEOPARDY!

NONFICTION

Clue	Value	Response
THIS "DILBERT" CANINE'S "TOP SECRET MANAGEMENT HANDBOOK" IS A HUMOROUS GUIDE FOR EXECUTIVES	$100	WHO IS
"A SIMPLE PATH" IS A COMPILATION OF THIS NOBEL PRIZE-WINNING NUN'S THOUGHTS & EXPERIENCES	$200	WHO IS
FOR THE WEEK OF OCTOBER 12, 1997, 3 OF THE TOP 4 N.Y. TIMES PAPERBACK BESTSELLERS WERE ABOUT HER	$300	WHO IS
IN "INTO THIN AIR" JON KRAKAUER SAID CLIMBING THIS MOUNTAIN "WAS PRIMARILY ABOUT ENDURING PAIN"	$400	WHAT IS
THIS SLUGGER PRAISED THE "ORIOLE WAY" OF TEACHING BASEBALL IN "THE ONLY WAY I KNOW"	$500	WHO IS

JEOPARDY!

NONFICTION

$100	WHO IS DOGBERT?	**$100**
$200	WHO IS MOTHER TERESA?	**$200**
$300	WHO IS PRINCESS DIANA?	**$300**
$400	WHAT IS MOUNT EVEREST?	**$400**
$500	WHO IS CAL RIPKEN, JR.?	**$500**

JEOPARDY!

SUPERSTITIONS

THIS APPENDAGE MAY BE CONSIDERED LUCKY, BUT NOT FOR THE ORYCTOLAGUS CUNICULUS	**$100**	WHAT IS
"FIND" ONE OF THESE & "PICK IT UP, ALL DAY LONG YOU'LL HAVE GOOD LUCK"	**$200**	WHAT IS
ST. PATRICK MIGHT HAVE TOLD A DIFFERENT STORY IF HE'D BEEN "LOOKING OVER" THIS LUCKY PLANT	**$300**	WHAT IS
TOSSING THIS AT NEWLYWEDS IS SUPPOSED TO ENSURE THE COUPLE'S FERTILITY	**$400**	WHAT IS
THIS MAN FOUNDED A RELIGION, SO GO AHEAD & RUB HIS TUMMY FOR LUCK	**$500**	WHO IS

JEOPARDY!™

SUPERSTITIONS

$100	WHAT IS A RABBIT'S FOOT?	**$100**
$200	WHAT IS A PENNY? (ACCEPT: PIN)	**$200**
$300	WHAT IS A FOUR-LEAF CLOVER?	**$300**
$400	WHAT IS RICE?	**$400**
$500	WHO IS BUDDHA?	**$500**

JEOPARDY!

SPORTS

Clue	Value	Response
THIS CHICAGO BULL SET A PLAYOFF RECORD WITH A 63-POINT GAME ON APRIL 20, 1986	$100	WHO IS
THIS NFL QUARTERBACK IS A GREAT-GREAT-GREAT-GRANDSON OF BRIGHAM YOUNG	$200	WHO IS
THE NABISCO DINAH SHORE IS ONE OF THE 4 EVENTS MAKING UP THE GRAND SLAM OF THIS SPORT FOR WOMEN	$300	WHAT IS
THIS OAKLAND A's & NEW YORK YANKEES OUTFIELDER HIT .357 WITH 10 HOME RUNS IN HIS 5 WORLD SERIES	$400	WHO IS
LAST NAME OF BROTHERS PHIL & TONY, BOTH NAMED TO THE HOCKEY HALL OF FAME	$500	WHAT IS

JEOPARDY!™

SPORTS

$100   WHO IS MICHAEL JORDAN?   **$100**

$200   WHO IS STEVE YOUNG?   **$200**

$300   WHAT IS GOLF?   **$300**

$400   WHO IS REGGIE JACKSON?   **$400**

$500   WHAT IS ESPOSITO?   **$500**

JEOPARDY!

NOT-SO-MAD SCIENTISTS

THE "E" IN HIS MOST FAMOUS EQUATION STANDS FOR ENERGY, NOT HIS NAME	**$100**	WHO IS
THIS MONK CONCEIVED THE LAWS OF HEREDITY WHILE MINDING HIS PEAS & Qs AS A TEACHER IN BRUNN, AUSTRIA	**$200**	WHO IS
JAMES WATSON & FRANCIS CRICK TEAMED UP TO DISCOVER THE DOUBLE HELIX STRUCTURE OF THIS	**$300**	WHAT IS
HIS DISCOVERIES PUBLISHED IN THE 1704 WORK "OPTICKS" EXPLAINED WHY OBJECTS APPEAR TO BE COLORED	**$400**	WHO IS
IN 1920 THIS DANE BECAME DIRECTOR OF THE INSTITUTE FOR THEORETICAL PHYSICS IN COPENHAGEN	**$500**	WHO IS

JEOPARDY!™

NOT-SO-MAD SCIENTISTS

$100	WHO IS ALBERT EINSTEIN?	**$100**
$200	WHO IS (GREGOR JOHANN) MENDEL?	**$200**
$300	WHAT IS DNA? (ACCEPT: DEOXY-RIBONUCLEIC ACID)	**$300**
$400	WHO IS SIR ISAAC NEWTON?	**$400**
$500	WHO IS NIELS BOHR?	**$500**

JEOPARDY!™

"C.C."

AT THIS FLORIDA SITE, THE SCIENTISTS ARE ALL OUT TO LAUNCH	$100	WHAT IS
HIS NAME, PRE-MUHAMMAD ALI	$200	WHO IS
COMPUTER DATABASES HAVE LARGELY REPLACED THIS LIBRARY RESOURCE	$300	WHAT IS
SLICES OF SALAMI, BOLOGNA, LIVERWURST, ETC.	$400	WHAT ARE
IN 1968 THIS LABOR LEADER HAD A GRAPE, ER . . . GRIPE	$500	WHO IS

37

JEOPARDY!™

"C.C."

$100 **WHAT IS CAPE CANAVERAL?** $100

$200 **WHO IS CASSIUS CLAY?** $200

$300 **WHAT IS A CARD CATALOG?** $300

$400 **WHAT ARE COLD CUTS?** $400

$500 **WHO IS CESAR CHAVEZ?** $500

DOUBLE JEOPARDY!

1910

Clue	Value	Response
KENT STATE & BOWLING GREEN STATE UNIVERSITIES OPENED IN THIS STATE IN 1910	$200	WHAT IS
THIS TRADE PAPER OF THE GARMENT INDUSTRY BEGAN PUBLISHING JULY 13, 1910	$400	WHAT IS
THE DESIGN OF THIS NYC RAILROAD STATION THAT OPENED IN 1910 WAS BASED ON THE ROMAN BATHS OF CARACALLA	$600	WHAT IS
THE AUTHOR OF "THE BATTLE HYMN OF THE REPUBLIC", SHE WENT MARCHING ON TO THE GREAT BEYOND OCT. 17, 1910	$800	WHO IS
IN 1910 E.M. FORSTER PUT A FINISH TO THIS NOVEL ABOUT A COUNTRY HOUSE	$1000	WHAT IS

DOUBLE JEOPARDY!

1910

$200   WHAT IS OHIO?   **$200**

$400   WHAT IS WOMEN'S WEAR DAILY? (ACCEPT: WWD)   **$400**

$600   WHAT IS PENN(SYLVANIA) STATION?   **$600**

$800   WHO IS JULIA WARD HOWE?   **$800**

$1000   WHAT IS "HOWARDS END"?   **$1000**

DOUBLE JEOPARDY!

LIBATIONS

IT'S THE MOST FAMOUS COCKTAIL WE KNOW WITH SINGAPORE IN ITS NAME	**$200**	WHAT IS
BE IT THE WHISKEY OR ANOTHER TYPE, THIS COCKTAIL SHOULD BE MADE WITH FRESH LEMON JUICE	**$400**	WHAT IS
WHISKEY & VERMOUTH ARE THE MAIN INGREDIENTS IN THE CLASSY COCKTAIL NAMED FOR THIS ISLAND	**$600**	WHAT IS
ON "M*A*S*H" TRAPPER JOHN ONCE ASKED A BARTENDER TO KEEP POURING THIS "HORRI-FYING" DRINK "UNTIL I TURN INTO ONE"	**$800**	WHAT IS
THIS YELLOW, ANISE-FLAVORED LIQUEUR IS AN ESSENTIAL INGREDIENT IN A HARVEY WALLBANGER	**$1000**	WHAT IS

DOUBLE JEOPARDY!

LIBATIONS

$200	WHAT IS A SINGAPORE SLING?	**$200**
$400	WHAT IS A SOUR?	**$400**
$600	WHAT IS MANHATTAN?	**$600**
$800	WHAT IS A ZOMBIE?	**$800**
$1000	WHAT IS GALLIANO?	**$1000**

DOUBLE JEOPARDY!

TIM CONWAY FILMS

Clue	Value	Response
TIM APPEARED WITH SANDRA BULLOCK IN THE 1997 SEQUEL TO THIS FILM, BUT HE DIDN'T REPLACE KEANU REEVES	$200	WHAT IS
IN 2 1960s MOVIES BASED ON THIS SERIES, TIM REPRISED HIS TV ROLE OF ENSIGN PARKER	$400	WHAT IS
TIM TEAMED UP WITH THIS FELLOW TV COMEDIAN IN SEVERAL FILMS INCLUDING 1980's "THE PRIVATE EYES"	$600	WHO IS
TIM HELPS A SHAPE-SHIFTING DEAN JONES RUN FOR OFFICE IN THIS SEQUEL TO "THE SHAGGY DOG"	$800	WHAT IS
IN A 1975 FILM, TIM PLAYED AMOS, A BUMBLING BANK ROBBER, WHO JOINS THIS TITLE GANG NAMED FOR A DESSERT	$1000	WHAT IS

DOUBLE JEOPARDY!

TIM CONWAY FILMS

$200   WHAT IS "SPEED"? $200

$400   WHAT IS "McHALE'S NAVY"? $400

$600   WHO IS DON KNOTTS? $600

$800   WHAT IS "THE SHAGGY D.A."? $800

$1000   WHAT IS "THE APPLE DUMPLING GANG"? $1000

DOUBLE JEOPARDY!

COMMON BONDS

SPY, LOOKING, STAINED	$200	WHAT ARE
BACHELOR'S, PANIC, BELLY	$400	WHAT ARE
UNSTIRRED MARTINIS, A LEG, YOUR BOOTY	$600	WHAT ARE
SHOULDER, ROLLER, SLING	$800	WHAT ARE
RIVER, SNOW, BLOOD	$1000	WHAT ARE

DOUBLE JEOPARDY!

COMMON BONDS

$200 | WHAT ARE TYPES OF GLASS? | $200

$400 | WHAT ARE BUTTONS? | $400

$600 | WHAT ARE THINGS YOU SHAKE? | $600

$800 | WHAT ARE BLADES? | $800

$1000 | WHAT ARE BANKS? | $1000

DOUBLE JEOPARDY!

AT EASEL

PICASSO'S "GUERNICA" WAS INSPIRED BY THE BOMBING OF A TOWN IN THIS, HIS NATIVE COUNTRY	**$200**	WHAT IS
THIS DUTCHMAN WHO DIED IN 1669 GAVE US PERHAPS THE MOST PENETRATING SELF-PORTRAITS IN ALL OF ART	**$400**	WHO IS
HEH-HEH, HEH-HEH, THIS CARTOONIST WHO CREATED "BEAVIS AND BUTT-HEAD" WAS INFLUENCED BY MONTY PYTHON	**$600**	WHO IS
THE FIRST NAME OF PROTO-BAROQUE PAINTER CARAVAGGIO, & OF RENAISSANCE PAINTER-SCULPTOR BUONAROTTI	**$800**	WHAT IS
BORN IN 1869, HE EXCELLED AS A POINTILLIST, A FAUVIST & FINALLY, AS A COLLAGIST	**$1000**	WHO IS

DOUBLE JEOPARDY!

AT EASEL

$200 WHAT IS SPAIN? $200

$400 WHO IS REMBRANDT (VAN RIJN)? $400

$600 WHO IS MIKE JUDGE? $600

$800 WHAT IS MICHELANGELO? $800

$1000 WHO IS HENRI MATISSE? $1000

DOUBLE JEOPARDY!

OH, POOH!

HE WAS AUTHOR A.A. MILNE'S SON IN REAL LIFE, POOH'S OWNER IN FICTION	$200	WHO IS
THIS SWEET IS POOH'S FAVORITE FOOD	$400	WHAT IS
THIS DONKEY FRIEND OF POOH LATER PUT OUT A "GLOOMY LITTLE INSTRUCTION BOOK"	$600	WHO IS
ERNEST H. SHEPARD CONTRIBUTED TO THE ORIGINAL POOH BOOKS IN THIS CAPACITY	$800	WHAT IS
IT'S THE "SIZABLE" FOREST WHERE WINNIE-THE-POOH & HIS FRIENDS LIVE	$1000	WHAT IS

DOUBLE JEOPARDY!

OH, POOH!

$200 WHO IS CHRISTOPHER ROBIN (MILNE)? **$200**

$400 WHAT IS HONEY? **$400**

$600 WHO IS EEYORE? **$600**

$800 WHAT IS THE ILLUSTRATOR? **$800**

$1000 WHAT IS THE HUNDRED ACRE WOOD? **$1000**

FINAL JEOPARDY!
FAMOUS STRUCTURES

IN 1930 THE CHRYSLER
BUILDING SURPASSED THIS
FOREIGN STRUCTURE BY
OVER 60 FEET TO BECOME
THE WORLD'S TALLEST

WHAT IS

FINAL JEOPARDY!
FAMOUS STRUCTURES

WHAT IS THE EIFFEL TOWER?

JEOPARDY!™

YOU GO, GIRL!

Clue	Value	Response
IT WAS THE MAIN CLAIM TO FAME OF A 26-YEAR-OLD RUSSIAN WOMAN NAMED VALENTINA TERESHKOVA	$100	WHAT IS
KNOWN AS "FLO JO", AT THE 1988 OLYMPICS SHE COULD GO LIKE NO OTHER GIRL	$200	WHO IS
JEANA, A PILOT ON THE FIRST NONSTOP, NON-REFUELING AROUND-THE-WORLD FLIGHT, SHARES THIS LAST NAME WITH SUPERPILOT CHUCK	$300	WHAT IS
SHE SET ALL KINDS OF SPEED RECORDS BEFORE DISAPPEARING IN JULY 1937	$400	WHO IS
IN THIS WORK, ONE OF THE BIG TALKERS ON THEIR WAY TO BECKET'S TOMB IS A PRIORESS, MADAME EGLENTYN	$500	WHAT IS

JEOPARDY!™

YOU GO, GIRL!

$100	WHAT IS THE FIRST WOMAN IN SPACE?	**$100**
$200	WHO IS FLORENCE GRIFFITH JOYNER?	**$200**
$300	WHAT IS YEAGER?	**$300**
$400	WHO IS AMELIA EARHART?	**$400**
$500	WHAT IS "THE CANTERBURY TALES"?	**$500**

JEOPARDY!™

MUSIC POTPOURRI

"ANATOMICAL" TERM FOR THE PART OF A STRING INSTRUMENT WHERE YOU'LL FIND THE FINGERBOARD	**$100**	WHAT IS
SOME PIANOS HAVE A THIRD, "SUSTAINING" ONE OF THESE	**$200**	WHAT IS
ON SHEET MUSIC, ff STANDS FOR THIS ITALIAN WORD THAT MEANS "VERY LOUD"	**$300**	WHAT IS
THIS FAMOUS SINGING GROUP BASED IN AUSTRIA'S CAPITAL WAS FOUNDED OVER 500 YEARS AGO, IN 1498	**$400**	WHAT IS
BEETHOVEN CALLED IT "SONATA QUASI UNA FANTASIA", BUT WE KNOW IT BY THIS "LUNAR" NAME	**$500**	WHAT IS

JEOPARDY!

MUSIC POTPOURRI

$100 — WHAT IS THE NECK? — $100

$200 — WHAT IS A PEDAL? — $200

$300 — WHAT IS FORTISSIMO? — $300

$400 — WHAT IS THE VIENNA BOYS' CHOIR? — $400

$500 — WHAT IS "MOONLIGHT SONATA"? — $500

JEOPARDY!™

SCIENTIFIC NAMES

Clue	Value	Response
LITTLE RED RIDING HOOD COULD TELL YOU IT'S KNOWN AS CANIS LUPUS	$100	WHAT IS
THE DOMESTIC TYPE OF THIS ANIMAL IS EQUUS CABALLUS	$200	WHAT IS
PANTHERA LEO, IT'S SEEN BEFORE MGM FILMS	$300	WHAT IS
THIS WHITE CREATURE IS URSUS MARITIMUS	$400	WHAT IS
WE SUPPOSE THIS BIRD, MEGADYPTES ANTIPODES, IS NAMED PARTLY FOR ITS NATIVE REGION	$500	WHAT IS

JEOPARDY!

SCIENTIFIC NAMES

$100	WHAT IS THE (GRAY OR TIMBER) WOLF?	**$100**
$200	WHAT IS THE HORSE?	**$200**
$300	WHAT IS THE LION?	**$300**
$400	WHAT IS THE POLAR BEAR?	**$400**
$500	WHAT IS THE PENGUIN?	**$500**

JEOPARDY!™

BOND WOMEN

THE COLOR SHIRLEY EATON WAS PAINTED ALL OVER HER BODY	**$100**	WHAT IS
AS JAMES BOND'S OLD FLAME, TERI HATCHER WAS PUT OUT IN THIS 1997 FILM	**$200**	WHAT IS
THIS SWISS BOMBSHELL SET THE STYLE FOR GIRLS TO COME WITH HER BODY OF WORK AS HONEY RYDER IN "DR. NO"	**$300**	WHO IS
THIS "LICENSE TO KILL" CO-STAR LATER GOT A LICENSE TO PRACTICE "LAW AND ORDER"	**$400**	WHO IS
NATALIE'S SISTER, SHE WAS PLENTY O'TOOLE IN "DIAMONDS ARE FOREVER"	**$500**	WHO IS

JEOPARDY!

BOND WOMEN

$100	WHAT IS GOLD?	**$100**
$200	WHAT IS "TOMORROW NEVER DIES"?	**$200**
$300	WHO IS URSULA ANDRESS?	**$300**
$400	WHO IS CAREY LOWELL?	**$400**
$500	WHO IS LANA WOOD?	**$500**

JEOPARDY!

U.S. GEOGRAPHY

Clue	Value	Response
IT'S THE ONLY STATE LYING SOUTH OF THE TROPIC OF CANCER	$100	WHAT IS
THIS 36-MILE-LONG RIVER PROVIDES PART OF THE BORDER BETWEEN NEW YORK & ONTARIO	$200	WHAT IS
THIS HISTORIC GEORGIA PORT LIES ON A RIVER OF THE SAME NAME, 18 MILES INLAND FROM THE ATLANTIC	$300	WHAT IS
THIS ARTIFICIAL LAKE IS NEVADA'S ONLY LAKE WITH AN OUTLET TO THE SEA	$400	WHAT IS
RHODE ISLAND'S SAKONNET & SEEKONK RIVERS ARE REALLY SALTWATER ARMS OF THIS BAY	$500	WHAT IS

JEOPARDY!™

U.S. GEOGRAPHY

$100 WHAT IS HAWAII? $100

$200 WHAT IS THE NIAGARA RIVER? $200

$300 WHAT IS SAVANNAH? $300

$400 WHAT IS LAKE MEAD? $400

$500 WHAT IS NARRAGANSETT BAY? $500

JEOPARDY!™

BEFORE & AFTER

THE ONETIME FLYING NUN WHO LANDS ON A MAGICAL BASEBALL DIAMOND ON YOUR FARM	**$100**	WHO IS
VAMPIRE LESTAT CREATOR WHO'S A "SAN FRANCISCO TREAT"	**$200**	WHO IS
DISAFFECTED GROUP BORN AFTER 1965 WHO ARE INVESTIGATED BY MULDER & SCULLY	**$300**	WHAT IS
THE LEAD SINGER OF THE MIRACLES WHO WAS STRANDED ON A DESERT ISLAND	**$400**	WHO IS
A BASKIN-ROBBINS TREAT USED FOR TOP SECRET DISCUSSION ON "GET SMART"	**$500**	WHAT IS

JEOPARDY!™

BEFORE & AFTER

$100 — WHO IS SALLY FIELD OF DREAMS? — $100

$200 — WHO IS ANNE RICE-A-RONI? — $200

$300 — WHAT IS GENERATION X-FILES? (ACCEPT: GEN X-FILES) — $300

$400 — WHO IS SMOKEY ROBINSON CRUSOE? — $400

$500 — WHAT IS THE ICE CREAM CONE OF SILENCE? — $500

DOUBLE JEOPARDY!

GOOD WILL SHAKESPEARE

WILL SHAKESPEARE'S FATHER JOHN WAS A BUSINESSMAN IN THIS TOWN & ONCE HELD AN OFFICE EQUAL TO MAYOR	**$200**	WHAT IS
WILL'S CHILDREN HAMNET & JUDITH WERE THESE, LIKE DROMIO & DROMIO IN "THE COMEDY OF ERRORS"	**$400**	WHAT ARE
WILL'S BIRTH IS CELEBRATED ON APRIL 23 PARTLY BECAUSE THAT'S THE FEAST DAY OF THIS PATRON SAINT OF ENGLAND	**$600**	WHO IS
IN LONDON SHAKESPEARE BOARDED WITH THE MOUNTJOYS, A FAMILY OF THESE FRENCH PROTESTANTS	**$800**	WHAT ARE
A PERPLEXING BEQUEST IN WILL'S WILL LEFT WIFE ANNE THE SECOND-BEST ONE OF THESE	**$1000**	WHAT IS

DOUBLE JEOPARDY!

GOOD WILL SHAKESPEARE

$200	WHAT IS STRATFORD (UPON AVON)?	**$200**
$400	WHAT ARE TWINS?	**$400**
$600	WHO IS ST. GEORGE?	**$600**
$800	WHAT ARE HUGUENOTS?	**$800**
$1000	WHAT IS A BED?	**$1000**

DOUBLE JEOPARDY!™

NAMES IN THE NUDE

ON A MEMORABLE AWARDS SHOW, JIM CARREY MODELED THIS BIBLICAL ACCESSORY & SAID, "THIS IS WHERE FASHION BEGAN"	**$200**	WHAT IS
THIS MODEL LOOKED M'M! M'M! GOOD IN THE DECEMBER 1999 ISSUE OF PLAYBOY	**$400**	WHO IS
IN 1997 BRAD PITT SUED THIS MAGAZINE FOR PUBLISHING NUDE PHOTOS OF HIM	**$600**	WHAT IS
ROBERT CARLYLE & MARK ADDY WERE 2 STARS OF THIS BRITISH FILM ABOUT HAPLESS MALE STRIPPERS	**$800**	WHAT IS
DEMI MOORE SHED HER CLOTHES & HER HAIR TO PLAY A NAVY SEAL IN THIS 1997 FILM	**$1000**	WHAT IS

DOUBLE JEOPARDY!

NAMES IN THE NUDE

$200 · WHAT IS A FIG LEAF? · **$200**

$400 · WHO IS NAOMI CAMPBELL? · **$400**

$600 · WHAT IS PLAYGIRL? · **$600**

$800 · WHAT IS "THE FULL MONTY"? · **$800**

$1000 · WHAT IS "G.I. JANE"? · **$1000**

DOUBLE JEOPARDY!

19th CENTURY AMERICA

IN 1849 STAGECOACH MAIL DELIVERY SERVICE WAS INTRODUCED ON THIS TRAIL BETWEEN MISSOURI & NEW MEXICO	**$200**	WHAT IS
THESE 2 MEN FOUGHT A FATAL DUEL ON JULY 11, 1804 IN WEEHAWKEN, NEW JERSEY	**$400**	WHO ARE
ON DEC. 15, 1893 DVORAK'S 9th SYMPHONY, KNOWN AS THIS, WAS PREMIERED BY THE N.Y. PHILHARMONIC	**$600**	WHAT IS
ON MAR. 29, 1882 THIS FIRST FRATERNAL SOCIETY OF CATHOLIC MEN WAS FOUNDED IN NEW HAVEN, CONNECTICUT	**$800**	WHAT IS
THIS 1803 CASE WAS THE FIRST IN WHICH THE SUPREME COURT DECLARED AN ACT OF CONGRESS UNCONSTITUTIONAL	**$1000**	WHAT IS

DOUBLE JEOPARDY!

19th CENTURY AMERICA

$200	WHAT IS THE SANTA FE TRAIL?	$200
$400	WHO ARE AARON BURR & ALEXANDER HAMILTON?	$400
$600	WHAT IS THE "NEW WORLD" SYMPHONY?	$600
$800	WHAT IS THE KNIGHTS OF COLUMBUS?	$800
$1000	WHAT IS MARBURY VS. MADISON?	$1000

DOUBLE JEOPARDY!

ICE CREAM

IN 1988 A 4 1/2-MILE ONE OF THESE FRUITY DESSERTS WAS CREATED IN PENNSYLVANIA	**$200**	WHAT IS
MINTY PYTHON & CHOC NESS MONSTER WERE SUGGESTIONS FOR THIS DUO'S NEW BRITISH FLAVOR	**$400**	WHO ARE
MID-20th CENTURY ELECTRIC REFRIG-ERATORS MEANT NO MORE WAITING FOR FROZEN TREATS UNTIL HE COMETH	**$600**	WHAT IS
THIS CHAIN ONCE BOASTED OVER 1,000 RESTAURANTS SERVING 28 FLAVORS WITH 16% BUTTERFAT	**$800**	WHAT IS
IN THE 1980s RESTAURATEUR DAVID MINTZ BEGAN MARKETING SOY ICE CREAM UNDER THIS BRAND NAME	**$1000**	WHAT IS

DOUBLE JEOPARDY!™

ICE CREAM

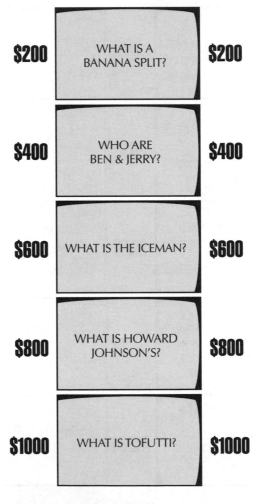

$200   WHAT IS A BANANA SPLIT?   **$200**

$400   WHO ARE BEN & JERRY?   **$400**

$600   WHAT IS THE ICEMAN?   **$600**

$800   WHAT IS HOWARD JOHNSON'S?   **$800**

$1000   WHAT IS TOFUTTI?   **$1000**

DOUBLE JEOPARDY!

NOTORIOUS

A BOOK ON THIS NIXON VICE PRESIDENT'S FORCED RESIGNATION WAS TITLED "A HEARTBEAT AWAY"	**$200**	WHO IS
AFTER KILLING THIS CRIMINAL FOR THE $10,000 REWARD, BOB FORD MADE PERSONAL APPEARANCES & WAS BOOED	**$400**	WHO IS
HE WAS HANGED, DRAWN & QUARTERED IN FRONT OF PARLIAMENT JAN. 31, 1606; NOT A GOOD "DAY" FOR HIM	**$600**	WHO IS
AN ASSASSIN'S AX ENDED THE LIFE OF THIS RUSSIAN REVOLUTIONARY IN MEXICO IN 1940	**$800**	WHO IS
THIS MAFIOSO TURNED SONGBIRD IN THE '60s WITH HIS TESTIMONY & HIS 1968 "PAPERS"	**$1000**	WHO IS

DOUBLE JEOPARDY!

NOTORIOUS

$200	WHO IS SPIRO AGNEW?	$200
$400	WHO IS JESSE JAMES?	$400
$600	WHO IS GUY FAWKES?	$600
$800	WHO IS LEON TROTSKY?	$800
$1000	WHO IS JOSEPH VALACHI?	$1000

DOUBLE JEOPARDY!

ANT-ONYMS

MOST MEMBERS OF AN ANT COLONY ARE THESE, AS OPPOSED TO RESTERS	**$200**	WHAT ARE
LIKE TERMITES, ANTS ARE THIS TYPE OF INSECT, NOT SOLITARY	**$400**	WHAT IS
IF YOU WANT A MOUND BUILT TO DAMAGE FARM MACHINERY, HIRE THESE ANTS WHOSE NAME IS AN ANTONYM OF "HIRE"	**$600**	WHAT ARE
AMAZON ANTS BECOME MASTERS WHEN THEY STEAL THE YOUNG FROM OTHER NESTS & MAKE THEM THESE	**$800**	WHAT ARE
THE EXTINCT PASSENGER PIGEON & THIS AFRICAN ARMY ANT ARE BOTH KNOWN FOR MOVING IN HUGE SWARMS	**$1000**	WHAT IS

DOUBLE JEOPARDY!™

ANT-ONYMS

$200	WHAT ARE WORKERS?	**$200**
$400	WHAT IS SOCIAL?	**$400**
$600	WHAT ARE FIRE ANTS?	**$600**
$800	WHAT ARE SLAVES?	**$800**
$1000	WHAT IS THE DRIVER ANT?	**$1000**

ISLANDS

THIS ISLE IS ROUGHLY AT THE CENTER OF THE TRIANGLE FORMED BY DUBLIN, GLASGOW & LIVERPOOL

WHAT IS

FINAL JEOPARDY!

ISLANDS

WHAT IS THE ISLE OF MAN?

JEOPARDY!™

PENNSYLVANIA

IT WAS AT THIS COLD HISTORIC SITE THAT VON STEUBEN REORGANIZED OUR ARMY IN FEBRUARY 1778	**$100**	WHAT IS
ONE OF ITS MORE UNIMAGINATIVE NICKNAMES IS "THE CAPITAL OF THE KEYSTONE STATE"	**$200**	WHAT IS
PITTSBURGH'S CIVIC ARENA WAS THE FIRST PUBLIC AUDITORIUM TO HAVE A RETRACT-ABLE ONE OF THESE	**$300**	WHAT IS
PHILADELPHIA'S MAJOR LEAGUE TEAMS INCLUDE THE PHILLIES, EAGLES, 76ers & THIS HOCKEY TEAM	**$400**	WHO ARE
THIS PORT CITY DISPLAYS A RECON-STRUCTION OF OLIVER HAZARD PERRY'S SHIP, THE NIAGARA	**$500**	WHAT IS

JEOPARDY!

PENNSYLVANIA

$100 WHAT IS VALLEY FORGE? $100

$200 WHAT IS HARRISBURG? $200

$300 WHAT IS A ROOF? $300

$400 WHO ARE THE FLYERS? $400

$500 WHAT IS ERIE? $500

JEOPARDY!™

ALMOST RHYMES WITH ORANGE

TO ADAPT EXISTING MUSIC FOR A PERFORMER, AS NELSON RIDDLE DID FOR FRANK SINATRA	**$100**	WHAT IS
A CEREAL COOKED IN WATER OR MILK & EATEN FOR BREAKFAST; BABY BEAR'S WAS "JUST RIGHT"	**$200**	WHAT IS
THIS ADJECTIVE MEANING "ALIEN" MIGHT RHYME WITH ORANGE IF YOU REVERSED THE FINAL "GN" & ADDED AN E	**$300**	WHAT IS
A TUBE FITTED WITH A PLUNGER & NEEDLE, USED TO INJECT FLUIDS	**$400**	WHAT IS
THE ITALIAN CITY OF THIS NAME HAS IL DUOMO; THE ONE IN SOUTH CAROLINA HAS THE PEE DEE EXPERIMENT STATION	**$500**	WHAT IS

JEOPARDY!™

ALMOST RHYMES WITH ORANGE

$100   WHAT IS ARRANGE? $100

$200   WHAT IS PORRIDGE? $200

$300   WHAT IS FOREIGN? $300

$400   WHAT IS A SYRINGE? $400

$500   WHAT IS FLORENCE? $500

JEOPARDY!

PRISON PROSE

Clue	Value	Response
IN "CIVIL DISOBEDIENCE", HE CALLED HIS NIGHT IN CONCORD JAIL "NOVEL AND INTERESTING ENOUGH"	$100	WHO IS
TITLE OF SISTER HELEN PREJEAN'S BOOK ABOUT DEATH ROW & THE SUSAN SARANDON FILM BASED ON IT	$200	WHAT IS
A WORK BY JEAN GENET STEMS FROM TIME AT THIS TYPE OF "SCHOOL", NAMED FOR WHAT IT TRIES TO DO TO YOUTHS	$300	WHAT IS
IN 1981 JAILED WRITER JACK HENRY ABBOTT WAS SPRUNG WITH THE HELP OF THIS "EXECUTIONER'S SONG" AUTHOR	$400	WHO IS
HITLER'S CHIEF ARCHITECT, HE WROTE "SPANDAU: THE SECRET DIARIES" OF HIS TIME IN PRISON FOR WAR CRIMES	$500	WHO IS

JEOPARDY!™

PRISON PROSE

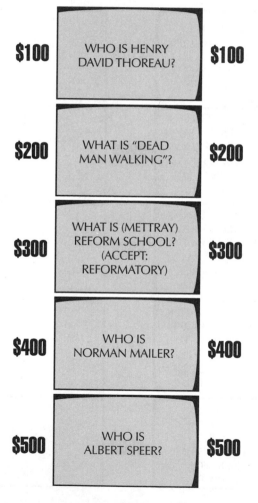

$100 — WHO IS HENRY DAVID THOREAU? — $100

$200 — WHAT IS "DEAD MAN WALKING"? — $200

$300 — WHAT IS (METTRAY) REFORM SCHOOL? (ACCEPT: REFORMATORY) — $300

$400 — WHO IS NORMAN MAILER? — $400

$500 — WHO IS ALBERT SPEER? — $500

JEOPARDY!™

TO THE NEAREST . . .

TO THE NEAREST 100, NUMBER OF YEARS THE UNITED STATES OF AMERICA HAS BEEN AN INDEPENDENT NATION	**$100**	WHAT IS
TO THE NEAREST FOOT, THE HEIGHT OF PATRICK EWING, ALONZO MOURNING OR RIK SMITS	**$200**	WHAT IS
TO THE NEAREST 10, THE BOILING POINT OF WATER IN FAHRENHEIT DEGREES	**$300**	WHAT IS
TO THE NEAREST BILLION, NUMBER OF COKES YOU'D NEED TO BUY TO GIVE ONE TO EVERYONE IN THE WORLD	**$400**	WHAT IS
TO THE NEAREST HOUR, FLIGHT TIME OF THE CONCORDE FROM LONDON TO NEW YORK	**$500**	WHAT IS

JEOPARDY!™

TO THE NEAREST . . .

$100	WHAT IS 200?	**$100**
$200	WHAT IS 7?	**$200**
$300	WHAT IS 210?	**$300**
$400	WHAT IS 6 (BILLION)?	**$400**
$500	WHAT IS 4?	**$500**

JEOPARDY!

SUPERMAN

THIS CUB REPORTER WAS CREATED FOR THE RADIO SERIES & LATER ADDED TO THE COMIC BOOK	**$100**	WHO IS
THE FAMOUS COVER OF ACTION COMICS NO. 1 SHOWS SUPERMAN LIFTING ONE OF THESE	**$200**	WHAT IS
RUMOR SAYS HE WAS SET TO DO ANOTHER SEASON OF "SUPERMAN" WHEN HE DIED IN 1959	**$300**	WHO IS
IN THE 1978 "SUPERMAN" MOVIE, GENE HACKMAN PLAYED THIS VILLAIN	**$400**	WHO IS
SUPERMAN HAS 2 SETS OF PARENTS: JONATHAN & MARTHA IN KANSAS, & LARA & THIS FATHER ON KRYPTON	**$500**	WHO IS

JEOPARDY!™

SUPERMAN

$100   WHO IS JIMMY OLSEN?   **$100**

$200   WHAT IS A CAR? (ACCEPT: SEDAN)   **$200**

$300   WHO IS GEORGE REEVES?   **$300**

$400   WHO IS LEX LUTHOR?   **$400**

$500   WHO IS JOR-EL?   **$500**

JEOPARDY!

3-LETTER SCIENCE

Clue	Value	Response
YOU'RE "WISER" IF YOU KNOW IT'S A SMALL POINTED STRUCTURE ON A STEM THAT GROWS INTO A FLOWER OR A LEAF	$100	WHAT IS
ABOUT 4.5 BILLION YEARS OLD, IT'S THE CLOSEST G2 TYPE STAR TO WHERE YOU'RE STANDING	$200	WHAT IS
YOU ADD THIS ELEMENT TO COPPER & ZINC TO GET BRONZE	$300	WHAT IS
A NEUTRAL ATOM WILL BECOME ONE OF THESE WHEN IT GAINS OR LOSES AN ELECTRON	$400	WHAT IS
IR"RESISTABLE" GERMAN PHYSICIST WITH A LAW ABOUT THE FLOW OF AN ELECTRIC CURRENT	$500	WHO WAS

JEOPARDY!™

3-LETTER SCIENCE

$100 — WHAT IS A BUD? — $100

$200 — WHAT IS THE SUN? — $200

$300 — WHAT IS TIN? — $300

$400 — WHAT IS AN ION? — $400

$500 — WHO WAS (GEORG SIMON) OHM? — $500

DOUBLE JEOPARDY!

ALL THE WORLD'S A STAGE

THIS CITY'S FAMED "ART THEATRE" OPENED IN 1898 WITH A PRODUCTION OF "CZAR FYODOR IVANOVICH"	**$200**	WHAT IS
THE 2-LETTER NAME OF THIS FORM OF JAPANESE DRAMA MEANS "TALENT" OR "SKILL"	**$400**	WHAT IS
SEVERAL OF HIS PLAYS, INCLUDING "LONG DAY'S JOURNEY INTO NIGHT", HAD THEIR WORLD PREMIERES IN STOCKHOLM	**$600**	WHO IS
THIS EXISTENTIALIST'S PLAY "THE FLIES", OR "LES MOUCHES", DEBUTED IN NAZI-OCCUPIED PARIS IN 1943	**$800**	WHO IS
THIS FAMED IRISH THEATRE THAT OPENED IN 1904 IS NAMED FOR THE STREET ON WHICH IT'S LOCATED	**$1000**	WHAT IS

DOUBLE JEOPARDY!

ALL THE WORLD'S A STAGE

$200 WHAT IS MOSCOW? **$200**

$400 WHAT IS NO? **$400**

$600 WHO IS EUGENE O'NEILL? **$600**

$800 WHO IS JEAN-PAUL SARTRE? **$800**

$1000 WHAT IS THE ABBEY THEATRE? **$1000**

DOUBLE JEOPARDY!

THE CARIBBEAN

Clue	Value	Response
IN 1992 SANTO DOMINGO'S QUINTO CENTENARIO CELEBRATION HONORED THIS EXPLORER'S DISCOVERY	**$200**	WHO IS
EVERY AUGUST THIS COUNTRY IS HOME TO THE REGGAE SUNSPLASH	**$400**	WHAT IS
EL YUNQUE, THE ONLY TRULY TROPICAL RAIN FOREST IN THE U.S. NATIONAL FOREST SYSTEM, IS ON THIS ISLAND POSSESSION	**$600**	WHAT IS
IT'S T&T TO THE NATIVES BUT DESMOND TUTU CALLED THIS NATION THE RAINBOW COUNTRY	**$800**	WHAT IS
THE DUTCH SIDE OF THIS ISLAND USES 110 VOLTS; THE FRENCH SIDE, 220	**$1000**	WHAT IS

DOUBLE JEOPARDY!

THE CARIBBEAN

$200   WHO IS CHRISTOPHER COLUMBUS?   **$200**

$400   WHAT IS JAMAICA?   **$400**

$600   WHAT IS PUERTO RICO?   **$600**

$800   WHAT IS TRINIDAD & TOBAGO?   **$800**

$1000   WHAT IS ST. MARTIN?   **$1000**

DOUBLE JEOPARDY!

FIRST NAMES

JUDGE ITO, OR A WEAPON	**$200**	WHO IS
THE "HEAVENLY" MS. BASSETT	**$400**	WHO IS
A MIGHTY WARRIOR, LIKE FOOTBALL'S PAYTON	**$600**	WHO IS
DECEMBER-BORN PLAYWRIGHT COWARD	**$800**	WHO IS
"FLOWERY" NOVELIST MURDOCH	**$1000**	WHO IS

DOUBLE JEOPARDY!

FIRST NAMES

$200   WHO IS LANCE? $200

$400   WHO IS ANGELA? $400

$600   WHO IS WALTER? $600

$800   WHO IS NOEL? $800

$1000   WHO IS IRIS? $1000

DOUBLE JEOPARDY!

R.E.M.

Clue	Value	Response
THE LINEUP 1980–1997: GUITARIST PETER BUCK, BASSIST MIKE MILLS, DRUMMER BILL BERRY & THIS SINGER	$200	WHO IS
THIS R.E.M. SONG GAVE A 1999 JIM CARREY MOVIE ITS TITLE	$400	WHAT IS
IN 1988 R.E.M. SAID "THAT'S ALL FOLKS!" TO I.R.S. RECORDS & SIGNED WITH THIS LABEL FOR BIG BUCKS	$600	WHAT IS
THE VIDEO FOR THE SONG TITLED "LOSING" THIS WAS BANNED IN IRELAND	$800	WHAT IS
R.E.M. FOLLOWED "NEW ADVENTURES IN HI-FI" WITH THIS ALBUM THAT HAS A 2-LETTER TITLE	$1000	WHAT IS

DOUBLE JEOPARDY!

R.E.M.

$200 — WHO IS MICHAEL STIPE? — $200

$400 — WHAT IS "MAN ON THE MOON"? — $400

$600 — WHAT IS WARNER BROS.? — $600

$800 — WHAT IS "(LOSING) MY RELIGION"? — $800

$1000 — WHAT IS "UP"? — $1000

DOUBLE JEOPARDY!

DISCOVERERS

IN THE 1570s THIS BRITISH CIRCUM-NAVIGATOR ATTACKED MANY SPANISH SHIPS AS A PIRATE IN THE CARIBBEAN	**$200**	WHO IS
THIS REAR ADMIRAL DISCOVERED A MOUNTAIN RANGE IN ANTARCTICA ON ONE OF HIS FAMOUS FLIGHTS OVER IT	**$400**	WHO IS
THIS MAN WHO SOUGHT THE SOURCE OF THE NILE WAS KNIGHTED IN 1886	**$600**	WHO IS
THIS PRIEST FIRST MET LOUIS JOLLIET WHEN JOLLIET ARRIVED AT HIS MISSION AT ST. IGNACE IN DECEMBER 1672	**$800**	WHO IS
IN 1497 THIS VENETIAN SAILING FOR ENGLAND BECAME THE FIRST EUROPEAN SINCE THE VIKINGS TO REACH N. AMERICA	**$1000**	WHO IS

DOUBLE JEOPARDY!

DISCOVERERS

$200	WHO IS SIR FRANCIS DRAKE?	**$200**
$400	WHO IS RICHARD EVELYN BYRD?	**$400**
$600	WHO IS SIR RICHARD FRANCIS BURTON?	**$600**
$800	WHO IS JACQUES MARQUETTE?	**$800**
$1000	WHO IS JOHN CABOT? (ACCEPT: GIOVANNI CABOTTO)	**$1000**

DOUBLE JEOPARDY!

HOMOPHONES

Clue	Value	Response
A CERTAIN CLOTHING ITEM, OR A TYPE OF ASIAN RESTAURANT THAT PROBABLY WON'T MAKE YOU WEAR ONE	$200	WHAT IS
IT'S WHAT'S NAMED FOR ZEBULON PIKE, OR THE BRIEF GLIMPSE HE GOT OF IT	$400	WHAT IS
WHAT HURRICANE ANDREW DID, OR HOW SOME PEOPLE FELT WHEN HE DID IT	$600	WHAT IS
A RED DEER, OR A BODY PART THAT MIGHT LEAP WHEN YOU SEE ONE	$800	WHAT IS
WHAT YOU DO TO A HOOK, OR WHAT YOU DO WITH YOUR BREATH WHILE WAITING FOR A FISH TO BITE	$1000	WHAT IS

DOUBLE JEOPARDY!

HOMOPHONES

$200	WHAT IS TIE/THAI?	**$200**
$400	WHAT IS PEEK/PEAK?	**$400**
$600	WHAT IS BLEW/BLUE?	**$600**
$800	WHAT IS A HART/HEART?	**$800**
$1000	WHAT IS BAIT/BATE?	**$1000**

FINAL JEOPARDY!

THE MOVIES

"A BOY'S LIFE" WAS THE
ORIGINAL TITLE OF THIS
1982 BLOCKBUSTER

WHAT IS

FINAL JEOPARDY!
THE MOVIES

WHAT IS "E.T.
(THE EXTRA-TERRESTRIAL)"?

JEOPARDY!

YANKEE INGENUITY

Clue	Value	Response
IT'S REPORTED THAT THE U.S. HAS ISSUED OVER 1870 PATENTS FOR THIS FLOWER; 400 OF THEM MENTION RED	$100	WHAT IS
THE MOTOR-DRIVEN PHONOGRAPH HE INVENTED IN 1888 PLAYED WAX CYLINDERS	$200	WHO IS
IN 1931 MILES LABORATORIES FIRST MARKETED THIS EFFERVESCENT TABLET	$300	WHAT IS
JOHN CURTIS MADE A SPRUCE-BASED TYPE IN 1848; THOMAS ADAMS MADE A CHICLE-BASED TYPE AROUND 1870	$400	WHAT IS
DU PONT SCIENTISTS ARE CREDITED WITH INVENTING THIS MATERIAL LATER USED TO DESCRIBE RONALD REAGAN & JOHN GOTTI	$500	WHAT IS

JEOPARDY!™

YANKEE INGENUITY

$100 — WHAT IS THE ROSE? — $100

$200 — WHO IS THOMAS EDISON? — $200

$300 — WHAT IS ALKA-SELTZER? — $300

$400 — WHAT IS CHEWING GUM? — $400

$500 — WHAT IS TEFLON? — $500

JEOPARDY!

"ACE" IN THE HOLE

Clue	Value	Response
INDIANA'S NBA TEAM	$100	WHO ARE
A RHYTIDECTOMY; IT'S A NIP & TUCK DONE ON THE MUG	$200	WHAT IS
A SPIKED MEDIEVAL WEAPON, OR A SPRAY THAT CAN HAVE NEARLY THE SAME EFFECT	$300	WHAT IS
ONE GOES BETWEEN THE DINNER PLATE & THE DINNER TABLE	$400	WHAT IS
WHALES, DOLPHINS & PORPOISES	$500	WHAT ARE

JEOPARDY!™

"ACE" IN THE HOLE

$100	WHO ARE THE PACERS?	$100
$200	WHAT IS A FACE-LIFT?	$200
$300	WHAT IS MACE?	$300
$400	WHAT IS A PLACE MAT?	$400
$500	WHAT ARE CETACEANS? (ACCEPT: CETACEA)	$500

JEOPARDY!

A SUPREME CATEGORY

Clue	Value	Response
GIVING YOUR LIFE FIGHTING FOR YOUR COUNTRY IS THE SUPREME ONE; A BUNT IS A LESSER ONE	$100	WHAT IS
HE WAS SUPREME COMMANDER OF ALLIED FORCES IN EUROPE, & LATER OF NATO FORCES	$200	WHO IS
MISSOURI'S MOTTO "SALUS POPULI SUPREMA LEX ESTO" MEANS THE PEOPLE'S WELFARE SHALL BE THE SUPREME THIS	$300	WHAT IS
IN A C.S. FORESTER NOVEL, THIS BRITISH SEA CAPTAIN HAS TO DEAL WITH A CRAZED DICTATOR NAMED EL SUPREMO	$400	WHO IS
FROM THE 1930s TO THE 1980s IT WAS THE 2-CHAMBERED LEGISLATURE OF THE USSR	$500	WHAT IS

JEOPARDY!™

A SUPREME CATEGORY

$100 WHAT IS A SACRIFICE? **$100**

$200 WHO IS DWIGHT D. EISENHOWER? **$200**

$300 WHAT IS LAW? **$300**

$400 WHO IS HORATIO HORNBLOWER? **$400**

$500 WHAT IS THE SUPREME SOVIET? (SUPREME COUNCIL) **$500**

JEOPARDY!™

BLOOD TEST

PEOPLE WHO LIVE AT HIGH ALTITUDES OFTEN HAVE THICKER BLOOD, TO DELIVER MORE OF THIS GAS TO BODY CELLS	**$100**	WHAT IS
THROMBOSES & EMBOLISMS ARE COMMON CAUSES OF STROKES, THE INTERRUPTION OF THE BLOOD SUPPLY TO THIS ORGAN	**$200**	WHAT IS
IF THIS "FACTOR" DIFFERS IN A PREGNANT WOMAN & HER FETUS, THE BABY'S RED BLOOD CELLS MAY BE DAMAGED	**$300**	WHAT IS
DOCTORS ARE AGAIN USING THESE BLOOD-SUCKING WORMS, NOW TO REMOVE CLOTS IN FINGERS REATTACHED BY MICROSURGERY	**$400**	WHAT ARE
TYPE AB IS CONSIDERED THE UNIVERSAL RECIPIENT; THIS TYPE IS THE UNIVERSAL DONOR	**$500**	WHAT IS

JEOPARDY!™

BLOOD TEST

$100	WHAT IS OXYGEN?	**$100**
$200	WHAT IS THE BRAIN?	**$200**
$300	WHAT IS THE RH FACTOR?	**$300**
$400	WHAT ARE LEECHES?	**$400**
$500	WHAT IS O?	**$500**

JEOPARDY!™

WOMEN'S WORK

IN 1977 KAY KOPLOVITZ FOUNDED WHAT BECAME THIS "PATRIOTIC" CABLE NETWORK, HOME TO "LA FEMME NIKITA"	**$100**	WHAT IS
THIS FUTURE SUPREME COURT JUSTICE HID HER PREGNANCY FOR FEAR OF LOSING HER TEACHING JOB AT RUTGERS	**$200**	WHO IS
THIS WOMAN NOT ONLY FOUNDED THE FIRST BIRTH CONTROL CLINIC, SHE ALSO PIONEERED THE TERM	**$300**	WHO IS
"AMERICA'S SWEET-HEART", SHE WAS JUST 24 IN 1917 WHEN SHE COMMANDED $350,000 PER FILM	**$400**	WHO IS
THIS LONGTIME WASHINGTON POST EDITOR & NEWSWEEK COMMENTATOR PASSED AWAY IN 1999	**$500**	WHO IS

JEOPARDY!™

WOMEN'S WORK

$100 WHAT IS THE USA NETWORK? **$100**

$200 WHO IS RUTH BADER GINSBURG? **$200**

$300 WHO IS MARGARET SANGER? **$300**

$400 WHO IS MARY PICKFORD? **$400**

$500 WHO IS MEG GREENFIELD? **$500**

JEOPARDY!™

1990s TELEVISION

FOX DRAMA ABOUT THE PLIGHT OF THE SALINGER CHILDREN, ORPHANED BY A CAR WRECK	**$100**	WHAT IS
THIS BILL MAHER GABFEST STARTED ON COMEDY CENTRAL & MOVED TO ABC	**$200**	WHAT IS
ROSLYN, WASHINGTON REPRESENTED CICELY, ALASKA, THE SETTING OF THIS ROB MORROW SERIES	**$300**	WHAT IS
THE QUIRKY DRAMA "PICKET FENCES" WAS SET IN THE TOWN OF ROME IN THIS STATE, NOT IN ITALY	**$400**	WHAT IS
"TWIN PEAKS" WAS THE FIRST TV VENTURE FOR THIS "ERASERHEAD" DIRECTOR	**$500**	WHO IS

JEOPARDY!™

1990s TELEVISION

$100	WHAT IS "PARTY OF FIVE"?	**$100**
$200	WHAT IS "POLITICALLY INCORRECT"?	**$200**
$300	WHAT IS "NORTHERN EXPOSURE"?	**$300**
$400	WHAT IS WISCONSIN?	**$400**
$500	WHO IS DAVID LYNCH?	**$500**

DOUBLE JEOPARDY!

HAIL, HAIL ALBANIA

IN THIS 1997 DUSTIN HOFFMAN FILM, THE U.S. WAGES A FICTIONAL WAR WITH ALBANIA	**$200**	WHAT IS
ALBANIA IS LOCATED ON THE EASTERN SHORES OF THE IONIAN SEA & THIS SEA	**$400**	WHAT IS
ALBANIA'S CAPITAL, IT CENTERS ON SKANDERBEG SQUARE	**$600**	WHAT IS
AFTER ALBANIA BROKE WITH THE USSR, IT TURNED TO THIS COUNTRY WHICH GAVE IT BILLIONS UNTIL A TIFF IN 1978	**$800**	WHAT IS
KING ZOG I RULED FROM 1928 UNTIL 1939, WHEN THIS COUNTRY ANNEXED ALBANIA	**$1000**	WHAT IS

DOUBLE JEOPARDY!

HAIL, HAIL ALBANIA

$200 WHAT IS "WAG THE DOG"? **$200**

$400 WHAT IS THE ADRIATIC SEA? **$400**

$600 WHAT IS TIRANE? **$600**

$800 WHAT IS CHINA? **$800**

$1000 WHAT IS ITALY? **$1000**

DOUBLE JEOPARDY!

CONTEMPORARIES

BURNT AT THE STAKE IN 1431, SHE WAS PROBABLY A PIN-UP GIRL FOR 11-YEAR-OLD TORQUEMADA	$200	WHO IS
WHILE JAMES WATT WAS GETTING STEAMED UP IN SCOTLAND, SHE WAS HEATING UP THE THRONE IN RUSSIA	$400	WHO IS
WHILE MONTEZUMA WAS RULING THE AZTECS, THIS POLE WAS MOVING THE SUN OUT OF THE CENTER OF THE UNIVERSE	$600	WHO IS
WHILE LEIF ERICSON HAD HIS FIRST LOOK AT THE NEW WORLD, THIS MAN WAS SITTING AS FIRST KING OF HUNGARY	$800	WHO IS
IN 1850 HAWTHORNE WROTE OF HESTER PRYNNE'S CRIME & THIS SCOT OPENED HIS CHICAGO DETECTIVE AGENCY	$1000	WHO IS

DOUBLE JEOPARDY!

CONTEMPORARIES

$200	WHO IS JOAN OF ARC?
$400	WHO IS CATHERINE THE GREAT? (ACCEPT: CATHERINE II)
$600	WHO IS NICOLAUS COPERNICUS?
$800	WHO IS (ST.) STEPHEN (I)?
$1000	WHO IS ALLAN PINKERTON?

DOUBLE JEOPARDY!

LET'S PLAY POKER

THE 2 BASIC TYPES OF POKER ARE DRAW & THIS ONE WITH CARDS DEALT UP & DOWN	**$200**	WHAT IS
IT'S THE REGAL NAME FOR A TEN, JACK, QUEEN, KING & ACE ALL OF ONE SUIT	**$400**	WHAT IS
2-WORD NAME FOR THE NEXT HAND IN VALUE BELOW FOUR OF A KIND	**$600**	WHAT IS
MANY PLAYERS HAVE TRIED THEIR LUCK AT THE WORLD SERIES OF POKER HELD IN THIS LAS VEGAS CASINO	**$800**	WHAT IS
IT'S A SEQUENCE SUCH AS THE FOUR, SIX, SEVEN & EIGHT, NEEDING ONE TANTALIZING CARD TO FILL IT	**$1000**	WHAT IS

DOUBLE JEOPARDY!

LET'S PLAY POKER

$200	WHAT IS STUD? (ACCEPT: OPEN)	**$200**
$400	WHAT IS A ROYAL FLUSH?	**$400**
$600	WHAT IS A FULL HOUSE?	**$600**
$800	WHAT IS (BINION'S) HORSESHOE?	**$800**
$1000	WHAT IS AN INSIDE STRAIGHT?	**$1000**

DOUBLE JEOPARDY!

MOVIE ADAPTATIONS

Clue	Value	Response
THE 2-WORD TITLE OF THIS CARL HIAASEN NOVEL BECAME ONE WORD WHEN DEMI MOORE DISROBED ON FILM	$200	WHAT IS
THIS BOGART-BERGMAN FILM IS BETTER REMEMBERED THAN ITS SOURCE, THE PLAY "EVERYBODY COMES TO RICK'S"	$400	WHAT IS
KEVIN KLINE & JOAN ALLEN WERE MOODY INDEED IN THIS "CHILLING" 1997 DRAMA FROM A RICK MOODY NOVEL	$600	WHAT IS
THIS FILM ABOUT A DYING CATCHER, BASED ON A MARK HARRIS NOVEL, TOOK ITS TITLE FROM "THE STREETS OF LAREDO"	$800	WHAT IS
1951's "A PLACE IN THE SUN" ADAPTS THIS CLASSIC "AMERICAN" NOVEL BY THEODORE DREISER	$1000	WHAT IS

DOUBLE JEOPARDY!

MOVIE ADAPTATIONS

$200	WHAT IS "STRIP TEASE"?	**$200**
$400	WHAT IS "CASABLANCA"?	**$400**
$600	WHAT IS "THE ICE STORM"?	**$600**
$800	WHAT IS "BANG THE DRUM SLOWLY"?	**$800**
$1000	WHAT IS "AN AMERICAN TRAGEDY"?	**$1000**

DOUBLE JEOPARDY!

HOW SUITE IT IS

AROUND 1725 THIS GREAT BAROQUE COMPOSER WROTE 6 "ENGLISH SUITES" FOR HARPSICHORD	**$200**	WHO IS
WHEN YOU LISTEN TO THIS FRENCH COMPOSER'S "MOTHER GOOSE" SUITE, WEAR A "BOLERO"	**$400**	WHO IS
THIS COMPOSER'S "PEER GYNT" SUITES BEGAN LIFE AS INCIDENTAL MUSIC FOR A PLAY BY HENRIK IBSEN	**$600**	WHO IS
GROFE'S 1931 SUITE NAMED FOR THIS ARIZONA SITE IS A LANDMARK IN AMERICAN MUSIC	**$800**	WHAT IS
"FAR EAST SUITE" IS AN IMPORTANT WORK BY THIS "NOBLE" BANDLEADER	**$1000**	WHO IS

DOUBLE JEOPARDY!

HOW SUITE IT IS

$200	WHO IS JOHANN SEBASTIAN BACH?	**$200**
$400	WHO IS MAURICE RAVEL?	**$400**
$600	WHO IS EDVARD GRIEG?	**$600**
$800	WHAT IS THE "GRAND CANYON SUITE"?	**$800**
$1000	WHO IS DUKE ELLINGTON?	**$1000**

DOUBLE JEOPARDY!

EPONYMS

SCIENTIST LUIGI GALVANI INSPIRED THIS WORD THAT CAN MEAN "TO SHOCK INTO ACTION"	**$200**	WHAT IS
ALTHOUGH HE LED THE ILL-FATED CHARGE OF THE LIGHT BRIGADE, THIS EARL IS BEST KNOWN FOR HIS SWEATER	**$400**	WHO IS
A CRACKER IS NAMED FOR THIS DIETARY REFORMER WHO ADVOCATED USING UNSIFTED WHOLE WHEAT FLOUR	**$600**	WHO IS
MANY SCHOLARS BELIEVE "O.K." COMES FROM "OLD KINDER-HOOK", THIS PRESI-DENT'S NICKNAME	**$800**	WHO IS
THESE -ISMS ARE NAMED FOR A CLERGYMAN WHO REPORTEDLY SAID THAT BEING FORCED TO RETIRE "CAME AS A BLUSHING CROW"	**$1000**	WHAT ARE

DOUBLE JEOPARDY!™

EPONYMS

$200	WHAT IS GALVANIZE?
$400	WHO IS (THE EARL OF) CARDIGAN?
$600	WHO IS (DR. SYLVESTER) GRAHAM?
$800	WHO IS MARTIN VAN BUREN?
$1000	WHAT ARE SPOONERISMS?

FINAL JEOPARDY!

PLAYS

BASED ON A MYTH,
THIS 1913 PLAY BECAME
A 1938 MOVIE, A 1956
STAGE MUSICAL & A 1964
MOVIE MUSICAL

WHAT IS

FINAL JEOPARDY!

PLAYS

WHAT IS "PYGMALION"?

JEOPARDY!

"N"ATIONS OF THE WORLD

MAKE A TREK TO UTRECHT & YOU'LL FIND YOURSELF IN THIS COUNTRY	**$100**	WHAT IS
ON THE FIRST MONDAY IN JUNE, THIS KIWI COUNTRY CELEBRATES THE QUEEN'S BIRTHDAY	**$200**	WHAT IS
THE PEOPLE OF THIS NATION HELPFULLY GAVE THEIR CAPITAL, MANAGUA, A NAME THAT RHYMES WITH THE COUNTRY	**$300**	WHAT IS
IT HAS A RAT NAMED FOR IT	**$400**	WHAT IS
IT BECAME FULLY INDEPENDENT OF SOUTH AFRICA MARCH 21, 1990	**$500**	WHAT IS

JEOPARDY!™

"N"ATIONS OF THE WORLD

$100 — WHAT IS THE NETHERLANDS? — $100

$200 — WHAT IS NEW ZEALAND? — $200

$300 — WHAT IS NICARAGUA? — $300

$400 — WHAT IS NORWAY? — $400

$500 — WHAT IS NAMIBIA? — $500

JEOPARDY!

PIG-OUT

ANGUAGELAY OKENSPAY ISTHAY AYWAY	**$100**	WHAT IS
THIS MUPPET WAS FEATURED IN HER OWN "GREAT LOVERS OF THE SILVER SCREEN" CALENDAR	**$200**	WHO IS
IN GERMAN THIS PROVERBIALLY FILTHY PLACE IS A "SCHWEINESTALL"	**$300**	WHAT IS
THIS PORCINE "GREEN ACRES" STAR WAS A REAL HAM; HE WON 2 PATSY AWARDS AS TV ANIMAL OF THE YEAR	**$400**	WHO IS
THE WALRUS SAID IT WAS TIME "TO TALK OF MANY THINGS", ABOUT "WHY THE SEA IS BOILING HOT AND WHETHER" THIS	**$500**	WHAT IS

JEOPARDY!™

PIG-OUT

$100	WHAT IS PIG LATIN?	**$100**
$200	WHO IS MISS PIGGY?	**$200**
$300	WHAT IS A PIGSTY?	**$300**
$400	WHO IS ARNOLD (ZIFFEL)?	**$400**
$500	WHAT IS "PIGS HAVE WINGS"?	**$500**

JEOPARDY!

IN THE SPIRIT

FRENCH FOR "A SITTING", IT'S A MEETING AT WHICH A MEDIUM TRIES TO COMMUNICATE WITH THE DEAD	**$100**	WHAT IS
THIS SHERLOCK HOLMES CREATOR BECAME AN ADVOCATE OF SPIRITUALISM AFTER HIS SON DIED IN WWI	**$200**	WHO WAS
CONSTANCE BENNETT & CARY GRANT APPEARED & DISAPPEARED IN THIS 1937 FILM CLASSIC	**$300**	WHAT IS
ROSEANNE & MADONNA ARE AMONG THE STARS WHO'VE STUDIED THIS JEWISH MYSTICAL TRADITION	**$400**	WHAT IS
POSSIBLY INHABITED BY A PIANO-PLAYING GHOST, THE STANLEY HOTEL IN COLORADO INSPIRED THIS STEPHEN KING TALE	**$500**	WHAT IS

JEOPARDY!™

IN THE SPIRIT

$100 | WHAT IS A SEANCE? | $100

$200 | WHO WAS SIR ARTHUR CONAN DOYLE? | $200

$300 | WHAT IS "TOPPER"? | $300

$400 | WHAT IS KABBALAH? (ACCEPT: ZOHAR) | $400

$500 | WHAT IS "THE SHINING"? | $500

JEOPARDY!

FIRST LADIES

SHE WAS FIRST LADY FOR 12 YEARS & 39 DAYS	**$100**	WHO IS
SHE ACTED AS A COVER FOR HER HUSBAND WHILE THE 1978 CAMP DAVID PEACE TALKS WENT ON LONGER THAN EXPECTED	**$200**	WHO IS
HER FIRST MARRIAGE WAS TO WILLIAM WARREN OF GRAND RAPIDS, MICHIGAN	**$300**	WHO IS
JULIA TYLER BEGAN THE CUSTOM OF HAVING THIS SONG PLAYED AS A PRESI-DENTIAL GREETING	**$400**	WHAT IS
IDA WENT WITH THIS MAN, HER HUSBAND, TO BUFFALO, BUT WASN'T PRESENT AT THE EXPOSITION WHERE HE WAS SHOT	**$500**	WHO IS

JEOPARDY!

FIRST LADIES

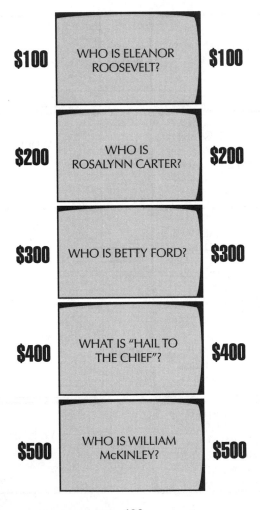

$100   WHO IS ELEANOR ROOSEVELT?   **$100**

$200   WHO IS ROSALYNN CARTER?   **$200**

$300   WHO IS BETTY FORD?   **$300**

$400   WHAT IS "HAIL TO THE CHIEF"?   **$400**

$500   WHO IS WILLIAM McKINLEY?   **$500**

JEOPARDY!™

PROVERBS

IT "MAKES A MAN HEALTHY, WEALTHY, AND WISE"	**$100**	WHAT IS
IN "THE WIZARD OF OZ", DOROTHY CLICKS HER HEELS & REPEATS THIS PROVERB BEFORE SHE'S WHISKED BACK TO KANSAS	**$200**	WHAT IS
IT "SELDOM KNOCKS TWICE", SO MAKE THE MOST OF IT	**$300**	WHAT IS
"BETTER THE FOOT SLIP THAN" THIS BODY PART	**$400**	WHAT IS
"MARRY IN HASTE, AND" DO THIS "AT LEISURE" (OR "IN RENO")	**$500**	WHAT IS

JEOPARDY!™

PROVERBS

$100	WHAT IS "EARLY TO BED AND EARLY TO RISE"?	**$100**
$200	WHAT IS "THERE'S NO PLACE LIKE HOME"?	**$200**
$300	WHAT IS OPPORTUNITY?	**$300**
$400	WHAT IS THE TONGUE?	**$400**
$500	WHAT IS REPENT?	**$500**

JEOPARDY!

COUNTRY MUSIC

IN 1980 THIS OCTOGENARIAN COMIC HIT THE COUNTRY CHARTS WITH "I WISH I WAS EIGHTEEN AGAIN"	**$100**	WHO IS
IT'S THE COUNTRY THAT COUNTRY STARS ANNE MURRAY & SHANIA TWAIN CAME FROM	**$200**	WHAT IS
ON HIS 1990 ALBUM "NO FENCES", HE SANG OF HAVING "FRIENDS IN LOW PLACES"	**$300**	WHO IS
SHEENA EASTON MADE IT TO THE COUNTRY CHARTS WHEN SHE DID THE DUET "WE'VE GOT TONIGHT" WITH THIS MAN	**$400**	WHO IS
A.P., SARA & MAYBELLE WERE THE HEART OF THIS, "THE FIRST FAMILY OF COUNTRY MUSIC"	**$500**	WHAT IS

JEOPARDY!™

COUNTRY MUSIC

$100	WHO IS GEORGE BURNS?	**$100**
$200	WHAT IS CANADA?	**$200**
$300	WHO IS GARTH BROOKS?	**$300**
$400	WHO IS KENNY ROGERS?	**$400**
$500	WHAT IS THE CARTER FAMILY?	**$500**

DOUBLE JEOPARDY!

REVELATIONS

MAKE WAY! MODERN SCIENCE HAS REVEALED THAT THIS PLANET TRAVELS AROUND THE SUN AT ABOUT 68,000 MPH	**$200**	WHAT IS
IN 1962 RACHEL CARSON REVEALED THE DANGERS OF TOXIC POLLUTION TO A MASS AUDIENCE IN THIS BOOK	**$400**	WHAT IS
USING LITMUS PAPER WILL REVEAL THE ACIDITY & ALKALINITY OF A SOLUTION ON A SCALE FROM 1 TO THIS NUMBER	**$600**	WHAT IS
THIS GERMAN'S EXCAVATIONS OF TROY IN THE 1870s REVEALED THE HOMERIC LEGENDS WERE NOT COMPLETELY A MYTH	**$800**	WHO IS
GREEK FOR "HEAT WRITING", THIS TECHNIQUE REVEALS ABNORMAL TISSUE GROWTH BY STUDYING TEMPERATURE	**$1000**	WHAT IS

DOUBLE JEOPARDY!™

REVELATIONS

$200	WHAT IS THE EARTH?	**$200**
$400	WHAT IS "SILENT SPRING"?	**$400**
$600	WHAT IS 14?	**$600**
$800	WHO IS HEINRICH SCHLIEMANN?	**$800**
$1000	WHAT IS THERMOGRAPHY?	**$1000**

DOUBLE JEOPARDY!

CHEESE, PLEASE

THIS MOST FAMOUS GREEK CHEESE IS SOMETIMES DESCRIBED AS "PICKLED" BECAUSE IT'S CURED IN BRINE	**$200**	WHAT IS
THIS TYPE OF GRATED CHEESE IS NAMED FOR ITALY'S CAPITAL	**$400**	WHAT IS
DE MEAUX IS A SUPERIOR TYPE OF THIS OOZING FRENCH CHEESE	**$600**	WHAT IS
THE "BABY" TYPE OF THIS DUTCH CHEESE, SIMILAR TO EDAM, IS USUALLY ENCASED IN RED WAX	**$800**	WHAT IS
SAMSOE IS A SWISS-STYLE COW'S MILK CHEESE NAMED FOR AN ISLAND IN THIS SCANDINAVIAN COUNTRY	**$1000**	WHAT IS

DOUBLE JEOPARDY!

CHEESE, PLEASE

$200 — WHAT IS FETA? — $200

$400 — WHAT IS ROMANO? — $400

$600 — WHAT IS BRIE? — $600

$800 — WHAT IS GOUDA? — $800

$1000 — WHAT IS DENMARK? — $1000

DOUBLE JEOPARDY!

AMERICAN ARTISTS

BEFORE TURNING TO PAINTING IN HER 70s, SHE EMBROIDERED PICTURES ON CANVAS	**$200**	WHO IS
IN 1963 THIS "CHRISTINA'S WORLD" PAINTER BECAME THE FIRST ARTIST TO RECEIVE THE PRESIDENTIAL MEDAL OF FREEDOM	**$400**	WHO IS
HIS PORTRAITS OF GEORGE WASHINGTON INCLUDE ATHENAEUM, VAUGHAN & HANDSDOWNE TYPES	**$600**	WHO IS
MANY OF HIS FAMOUS SEASCAPES WERE SET AT HIS HOME IN PROUT'S NECK, MAINE	**$800**	WHO IS
HIS WEB SITE SHOWS "BRILLIANTLY COLORED, STUNNINGLY ENER-GETIC IMAGES OF SPORTING EVENTS"	**$1000**	WHO IS

DOUBLE JEOPARDY!

AMERICAN ARTISTS

$200
WHO IS GRANDMA MOSES? (ANNA MARY ROBERTSON MOSES)
$200

$400
WHO IS ANDREW WYETH?
$400

$600
WHO IS GILBERT STUART?
$600

$800
WHO IS WINSLOW HOMER?
$800

$1000
WHO IS LEROY NEIMAN?
$1000

DOUBLE JEOPARDY!

FLAG-WAVING

Clue	Value	Response
THE GREEN FIELD ON THE FLAG OF BANGLADESH REPRESENTS THIS RELIGION	**$200**	WHAT IS
ALBANIA'S FLAG FEATURES A DOUBLE-HEADED ONE OF THESE BIRDS; AUSTRIA'S HAS JUST ONE HEAD	**$400**	WHAT IS
THIS COUNTRY'S COAT OF ARMS, SEEN ON ITS FLAG, DEPICTS A LEGENDARY AZTEC VISION	**$600**	WHAT IS
WANT TO KNOW WAT'S DEPICTED ON THIS COUNTRY'S FLAG? ANGKOR WAT, THAT'S WAT!	**$800**	WHAT IS
CONSTELLATION DEPICTED WITH 5 STARS ON THE FLAG OF WESTERN SAMOA	**$1000**	WHAT IS

DOUBLE JEOPARDY!

FLAG-WAVING

$200 WHAT IS ISLAM? **$200**

$400 WHAT IS AN EAGLE? **$400**

$600 WHAT IS MEXICO? **$600**

$800 WHAT IS CAMBODIA? **$800**

$1000 WHAT IS THE SOUTHERN CROSS? (ACCEPT: THE CRUX) **$1000**

DOUBLE JEOPARDY!

FAMILIAR QUOTATIONS . . . IN 1800

THIS 1726 NOVEL REPORTED THAT THE EMPEROR'S LARGEST HORSES WERE "EACH ABOUT FOUR INCHES AND A HALF HIGH"	**$200**	WHAT IS
ON NOV. 10, 1770 VOLTAIRE PENNED, "IF GOD DID NOT EXIST, IT WOULD BE NECESSARY TO" DO THIS	**$400**	WHAT IS
THIS BRITISH LEXICOGRAPHER CALLED JOHN DRYDEN "THE FATHER OF ENGLISH CRITICISM"	**$600**	WHO IS
THIS "CLASSY" SWEDE WROTE, "TO LIVE BY MEDICINE IS TO LIVE HORRIBLY"	**$800**	WHO IS
IN 1762 ROUSSEAU LAMENTED, "MAN IS BORN FREE, AND EVERYWHERE HE IS IN" THESE	**$1000**	WHAT ARE

DOUBLE JEOPARDY!

FAMILIAR QUOTATIONS . . . IN 1800

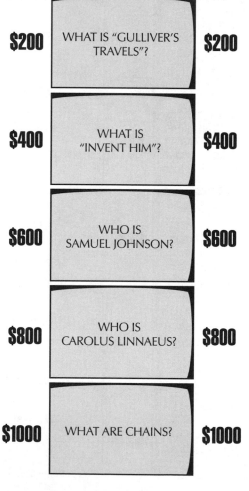

$200 WHAT IS "GULLIVER'S TRAVELS"? **$200**

$400 WHAT IS "INVENT HIM"? **$400**

$600 WHO IS SAMUEL JOHNSON? **$600**

$800 WHO IS CAROLUS LINNAEUS? **$800**

$1000 WHAT ARE CHAINS? **$1000**

DOUBLE JEOPARDY!

THE OLYMPICS

HELEN WILLS & STEFFI GRAF WERE CONSECUTIVE GOLD MEDALISTS IN THIS SPORT, 64 YEARS APART	**$200**	WHAT IS
ON FEB. 22, 1980 MIKE ERUZIONE SCORED THE WINNING GOAL AS THE U.S. BEAT THIS COUNTRY IN HOCKEY	**$400**	WHAT IS
IN 1992, AT AGE 13, CHINA'S FU MINGXIA WON THE WOMEN'S PLATFORM GOLD MEDAL IN THIS SPORT	**$600**	WHAT IS
IN 1904 AMERICAN THOMAS HICKS WON THIS RACE AFTER AN EMERGENCY DOSE OF BRANDY & STRYCHNINE PARTWAY THROUGH	**$800**	WHAT IS
IN 1998 HERMANN MAIER, KNOWN BY THIS ARNOLDIAN NICKNAME, GOT UP FROM A SKI CRASH TO WIN GOLD AT NAGANO	**$1000**	WHAT IS

DOUBLE JEOPARDY!™

THE OLYMPICS

$200 — WHAT IS (SINGLES) TENNIS? — $200

$400 — WHAT IS THE USSR? — $400

$600 — WHAT IS DIVING? — $600

$800 — WHAT IS THE MARATHON? — $800

$1000 — WHAT IS THE HERMINATOR? — $1000

FINAL JEOPARDY!

ACTORS & THEIR FILMS

THE TITLE OF RICHARD
BURTON'S LAST FEATURE
FILM, OR THE YEAR
IT WAS RELEASED

WHAT IS

FINAL JEOPARDY!

ACTORS & THEIR FILMS

WHAT IS "1984"?

JEOPARDY!

AUSTRALIA

Clue	Value	Response
AUSTRALIA BOASTS THE ONLY ALL-BLACK TYPE OF THIS OFTEN WHITE & GRACEFUL AQUATIC BIRD	**$100**	WHAT IS
THE GAME CALLED THE "AUSTRALIAN RULES" TYPE OF THIS IS PLAYED ON A FIELD UP TO 200 YARDS LONG WITH 4 POSTS AT EACH END	**$200**	WHAT IS
ONE OF AUSTRALIA'S BEST-KNOWN EXPORTS IS THIS MAN SEEN IN "CROCODILE DUNDEE" & IN SUBARU ADS	**$300**	WHO IS
THIS PARTY LED AUSTRALIA FROM 1983 TO 1996, WHILE A PARTY OF THE SAME NAME WAS BRITAIN'S OPPOSITION	**$400**	WHAT IS
5-LETTER NAME OF THE CAPITAL OF WESTERN AUSTRALIA, NAMED FOR A COUNTY IN SCOTLAND	**$500**	WHAT IS

JEOPARDY!™

AUSTRALIA

$100 WHAT IS THE SWAN? **$100**

$200 WHAT IS FOOTBALL? **$200**

$300 WHO IS PAUL HOGAN? **$300**

$400 WHAT IS THE LABOUR PARTY? **$400**

$500 WHAT IS PERTH? **$500**

JEOPARDY!

TASTE TREATS

U.S. CITY NOTED FOR ITS CREAM CHEESE & CHEESE STEAKS	**$100**	WHAT IS
ELMER DOOLIN BOUGHT THE RECIPE FOR THESE FRIED CORN MEAL CHIPS FOR $100 & BUILT AN EMPIRE	**$200**	WHAT ARE
THIS FORMER TALENT AGENT FOUNDED HIS COOKIE EMPIRE IN 1975, 2 YEARS BEFORE MRS. FIELDS	**$300**	WHO IS
IN 1989 THIS COMPANY INTRODUCED ITS SYMPHONY BAR	**$400**	WHAT IS
1948 SAW THE INTRODUCTION OF THIS BRAND, THE FIRST MAJOR U.S. AEROSOL FOOD PRODUCT	**$500**	WHAT IS

JEOPARDY!™

TASTE TREATS

$100	WHAT IS PHILADELPHIA?	$100
$200	WHAT ARE FRITOS?	$200
$300	WHO IS FAMOUS (WALLY) AMOS?	$300
$400	WHAT IS HERSHEY'S?	$400
$500	WHAT IS REDDI-WIP?	$500

JEOPARDY!

REPORTERS

Clue	Value	Response
SPORTSWRITER GRANTLAND RICE WROTE THAT THE "GREAT SCORER" MARKS "NOT THAT YOU WON OR LOST" BUT THIS	$100	WHAT IS
DURING THE GULF WAR WOLF BLITZER'S BEAT FOR CNN WAS THIS BUILDING WHERE HE SAW ALL SIDES OF AN ISSUE, NOT JUST 5	$200	WHAT IS
HIS BOOK "ANOTHER CITY, NOT MY OWN" IS BASED ON HIS TIME COVERING THE SIMPSON TRIAL FOR VANITY FAIR	$300	WHO IS
ROSCOE WAS THE MIDDLE NAME OF THIS MAN KNOWN FOR HIS CALM RADIO REPORTAGE DURING WWII	$400	WHO IS
THIS KING OF GONZO JOURNALISM WROTE OF "FEAR AND LOATHING IN LAS VEGAS" & IN THE 1972 CAMPAIGN	$500	WHO IS

JEOPARDY!™

REPORTERS

$100 · WHAT IS "HOW YOU PLAYED THE GAME"? · **$100**

$200 · WHAT IS THE PENTAGON? · **$200**

$300 · WHO IS DOMINICK DUNNE? · **$300**

$400 · WHO IS EDWARD R. MURROW? · **$400**

$500 · WHO IS HUNTER S. THOMPSON? · **$500**

JEOPARDY!

CANINE PROVERBS

COMPLETES THE TIMELY PROVERB "EVERY DOG HAS . . ."	**$100**	WHAT IS
IN OTHER WORDS, "THERE'S NO WAY TO EDUCATE ONE ANCIENT CANINE IN UP-TO-DATE ACTIONS"	**$200**	WHAT IS
"DOGS THAT" DO THIS "AT A DISTANCE SELDOM BITE"	**$300**	WHAT IS
IN LATIN IT'S "QUI ME AMAT, AMAT ET CANEM MEAM"	**$400**	WHAT IS
"INTO THE MOUTH OF A BAD DOG OFTEN FALLS A GOOD" ONE OF THESE	**$500**	WHAT IS

JEOPARDY!

CANINE PROVERBS

$100 — WHAT IS "HIS DAY"? — $100

$200 — WHAT IS "YOU CAN'T TEACH AN OLD DOG NEW TRICKS"? — $200

$300 — WHAT IS "BARK"? — $300

$400 — WHAT IS "LOVE ME, LOVE MY DOG"? — $400

$500 — WHAT IS A BONE? — $500

JEOPARDY!

SPACY POP MUSIC

IN 1979 STING & THIS GROUP WERE "WALKING ON THE MOON"	$100	WHAT IS
"SPACE ODDITY" WAS HIS FIRST U.S. TOP 10 HIT	$200	WHO IS
IN 1992 MEMBERS OF QUEEN HELD A TRIBUTE CONCERT FOR THIS LATE LEAD SINGER	$300	WHO IS
HE WAS BORN IN LIVERPOOL ON JULY 7, 1940	$400	WHO IS
PUBLIC ENEMY CALLED THEIR 1990 ALBUM "FEAR OF" THIS	$500	WHAT IS

JEOPARDY!

SPACY POP MUSIC

$100	WHAT IS THE POLICE?	$100
$200	WHO IS DAVID BOWIE?	$200
$300	WHO IS FREDDIE MERCURY?	$300
$400	WHO IS RINGO STARR?	$400
$500	WHAT IS "A BLACK PLANET"?	$500

JEOPARDY!

IT'S A GUY THING

GUYS LOVE THIS EYE-GOUGING COMEDY TEAM WHO STARTED IN VAUDEVILLE IN 1923 AS JUST A DUO	**$100**	WHO ARE
PROVERBIALLY, THEY'RE WHAT MEN HATE ASKING FOR, EVEN IF THEY END, "YOU CAN'T MISS IT"	**$200**	WHAT ARE
IT'S THE MAIN HOR-MONE PRODUCING MALE CHARACTERISTICS LIKE FACIAL HAIR & LOVE OF SPORTS CARS	**$300**	WHAT IS
IN 1990 COLORADO COACH BILL McCART-NEY FOUNDED THIS MOVEMENT OF CHRISTIAN MEN	**$400**	WHO ARE
THIS MAGAZINE CALLS ITSELF "THE BEST THING TO HAPPEN TO MEN SINCE WOMEN"	**$500**	WHAT IS

JEOPARDY!

IT'S A GUY THING

$100	WHO ARE THE THREE STOOGES?	**$100**
$200	WHAT ARE DIRECTIONS?	**$200**
$300	WHAT IS TESTOSTERONE?	**$300**
$400	WHO ARE THE PROMISE KEEPERS?	**$400**
$500	WHAT IS MAXIM?	**$500**

DOUBLE JEOPARDY!

CHARLES V

IN 1541 CHARLES LED A DOOMED NAVAL CAMPAIGN TO TAKE ALGIERS FROM THIS TURKISH EMPIRE	**$200**	WHAT IS
IN 1522 THIS MAN WROTE CHARLES THAT THE AZTECS "SAID THAT BY NO MEANS WOULD THEY GIVE THEMSELVES UP"	**$400**	WHO IS
IN 1530 CHARLES BECAME THE LAST OF THESE EMPERORS TO BE CROWNED BY A POPE	**$600**	WHAT IS
IN 1522 CHARLES INTRODUCED THIS SPANISH INSTITUTION TO THE NETHERLANDS TO PERSECUTE PROTESTANTS	**$800**	WHAT IS
CHARLES CONVENED THE DIET OF WORMS WHERE THIS MAN REFUSED TO RECANT HIS BELIEFS	**$1000**	WHO IS

DOUBLE JEOPARDY!

CHARLES V

$200 — WHAT IS THE OTTOMAN EMPIRE? — $200

$400 — WHO IS HERNAN CORTES? (ACCEPT: HERNANDO CORTEZ) — $400

$600 — WHAT IS A HOLY ROMAN EMPEROR? — $600

$800 — WHAT IS THE INQUISITION? — $800

$1000 — WHO IS MARTIN LUTHER? — $1000

DOUBLE JEOPARDY!

COMEDIES

IN 1998 THIS NBC SITCOM WITH JERRY, ELAINE, GEORGE & KRAMER SIGNED OFF THE NETWORK	**$200**	WHAT IS
THE '80s PUT LISA BONET & MALCOLM-JAMAL WARNER ON THE MAP AS 2 OF THIS COMEDIAN'S TV KIDS	**$400**	WHO IS
1997 FILM CONCERNING A CUTE DOG, A GAY ARTIST, AN EARTHY WAITRESS & A REALLY STRANGE AUTHOR	**$600**	WHAT IS
TITLE OF A RAY WALSTON SITCOM & A LATER CHRISTOPHER LLOYD MOVIE	**$800**	WHAT IS
LAST NAME OF FELICITY, HEATHER GRAHAM'S CHARACTER IN THE SECOND AUSTIN POWERS MOVIE— OH, BEHAVE!	**$1000**	WHAT IS

DOUBLE JEOPARDY!

COMEDIES

$200   WHAT IS "SEINFELD"?   **$200**

$400   WHO IS BILL COSBY?   **$400**

$600   WHAT IS "AS GOOD AS IT GETS"?   **$600**

$800   WHAT IS "MY FAVORITE MARTIAN"?   **$800**

$1000   WHAT IS SHAGWELL?   **$1000**

DOUBLE JEOPARDY!

SCIENCE & NATURE

FOUND IN EASTERN AUSTRALIA & TASMANIA, THIS MAMMAL'S SCIENTIFIC NAME MEANS "BIRD-SNOUT"	$200	WHAT IS
THIS METAL USED IN STORAGE BATTERIES IS REFINED MAINLY FROM A GRAY METALLIC ORE CALLED GALENA	$400	WHAT IS
THE RETINA HAS ABOUT 75 TO 150 MILLION RODS & ONLY ABOUT 7 MILLION OF THESE RECEPTOR CELLS	$600	WHAT ARE
THIS INERT GAS SYMBOLIZED Ar IS USED TO FILL LIGHT BULBS TO PREVENT THE TUNGSTEN FILAMENT FROM EVAPORATING	$800	WHAT IS
IN DIGITAL WATCHES, LCD STANDS FOR LIQUID CRYSTAL DISPLAY; LED STANDS FOR THIS	$1000	WHAT IS

DOUBLE JEOPARDY!™

SCIENCE & NATURE

$200 WHAT IS THE (DUCK-BILLED) PLATYPUS? **$200**

$400 WHAT IS LEAD? **$400**

$600 WHAT ARE CONES? **$600**

$800 WHAT IS ARGON? **$800**

$1000 WHAT IS LIGHT-EMITTING DIODE? (ACCEPT: LIQUID ELEMENT DISPLAY) **$1000**

DOUBLE JEOPARDY!

SCOTTISH LIT

THIS AUTHOR WHO DELIGHTED GENERATIONS WITH "PETER PAN" WAS SHORT, SHY & LONELY	**$200**	WHO IS
WITH "WAVERLEY" & "IVANHOE", HE ESTABLISHED THE GENRE OF THE HISTORICAL NOVEL	**$400**	WHO IS
THIS 1996 FILM ABOUT SCOTTISH DRUGGIES WAS BASED ON A NOVEL BY IRVINE WELSH	**$600**	WHAT IS
ROBERT LOUIS STEVENSON BASED THIS NOVEL ABOUT DAVID BALFOUR ON AN ACTUAL SCOTTISH CRIME	**$800**	WHAT IS
ONE OF THE FIRST MAJOR SCOTTISH POEMS WAS JOHN BARBOUR'S 1376 CHRONICLE OF THIS KING SOMETIMES CALLED "THE BRUCE"	**$1000**	WHO IS

DOUBLE JEOPARDY!

SCOTTISH LIT

$200	WHO IS (SIR) JAMES M. BARRIE?	**$200**
$400	WHO IS SIR WALTER SCOTT?	**$400**
$600	WHAT IS "TRAINSPOTTING"?	**$600**
$800	WHAT IS "KIDNAPPED"?	**$800**
$1000	WHO WAS ROBERT BRUCE? (ACCEPT: ROBERT I)	**$1000**

DOUBLE JEOPARDY!

CELEBRITY EXES

IN HAPPIER TIMES, THIS COUPLE FOUNDED DESILU PRODUCTIONS	**$200**	WHO ARE
IN THE '60s BARBRA STREISAND WAS MARRIED TO THIS ACTOR; THEIR SON JASON APPEARED IN "THE PRINCE OF TIDES"	**$400**	WHO IS
EVERYTHING DIDN'T COME UP ROSES FOR ERNEST BORGNINE & THIS ENTERTAINER; THEY SEPARATED AFTER A MONTH	**$600**	WHO IS
THIS FORMER WIFE OF NEIL SIMON HAS APPEARED AS MARTIN CRANE'S GIRLFRIEND SHERRY ON "FRASIER"	**$800**	WHO IS
JOHN DEREK'S PARTNERS INCLUDED THIS BLONDE "DYNASTY" ACTRESS	**$1000**	WHO IS

DOUBLE JEOPARDY!™

CELEBRITY EXES

$200 — WHO ARE LUCILLE BALL & DESI ARNAZ? — $200

$400 — WHO IS ELLIOTT GOULD? — $400

$600 — WHO IS ETHEL MERMAN? — $600

$800 — WHO IS MARSHA MASON? — $800

$1000 — WHO IS LINDA EVANS? — $1000

DOUBLE JEOPARDY!

"WATER"

THIS POISONOUS VIPER IS ALSO CALLED A COTTONMOUTH	**$200**	WHAT IS
THIS SERIES OF MONET WORKS WAS PAINTED NEAR THE END OF HIS LIFE WHEN HE WAS ALMOST BLIND	**$400**	WHAT IS
THE 23rd PSALM SAYS THE LORD "MAKETH ME TO LIE DOWN IN GREEN PASTURES: HE LEADETH ME" BESIDE THESE	**$600**	WHAT ARE
IN 1970 SIMON & GARFUNKEL SANG, "LIKE" THIS "I WILL LAY ME DOWN"	**$800**	WHAT IS
THIS IRISH CITY FOUNDED BY VIKING RAIDERS IN THE 800s IS BEST KNOWN FOR ITS GLASSWARE	**$1000**	WHAT IS

DOUBLE JEOPARDY!

"WATER"

$200 — WHAT IS A WATER MOCCASIN? — **$200**

$400 — WHAT IS "WATER LILIES"? — **$400**

$600 — WHAT ARE "THE STILL WATERS"? — **$600**

$800 — WHAT IS "A BRIDGE OVER TROUBLED WATER"? — **$800**

$1000 — WHAT IS WATERFORD? — **$1000**

FINAL JEOPARDY!

COUNTRIES OF THE WORLD

THE 3 MOST POPULOUS
COUNTRIES, THEY ADDED
UP TO AN ESTIMATED
2.4 BILLION PEOPLE
IN THE MID-'90s

WHAT ARE

FINAL JEOPARDY!
COUNTRIES OF THE WORLD

WHAT ARE CHINA,
INDIA & THE UNITED
STATES OF AMERICA?

JEOPARDY!™

THE OCEAN

Clue	Value	Response
THE NORTH POLE SITS NEAR THE CENTER OF THIS OCEAN	$100	WHAT IS
THE 2 BODIES WHOSE GRAVITATIONAL PULL ON THE EARTH HAS THE GREATEST EFFECT ON OCEAN TIDES	$200	WHAT ARE
THERE ARE 3 MAJOR TYPES OF THESE STRUCTURES IN THE TROPICS: FRINGING, BARRIER & ATOLLS	$300	WHAT ARE
THE CYANEA, A TYPE OF THIS CREATURE SCIENTISTS CALL THE MEDUSA, MAY HAVE 100-FOOT-LONG TENTACLES & NOT ONE BONE	$400	WHAT IS
YOU CROSS IT GOING FROM MOGADISHU TO THE MALDIVES	$500	WHAT IS

JEOPARDY!™

THE OCEAN

$100 | WHAT IS THE ARCTIC OCEAN? | **$100**

$200 | WHAT ARE THE SUN & THE MOON? | **$200**

$300 | WHAT ARE (CORAL) REEFS? | **$300**

$400 | WHAT IS A JELLYFISH? (ACCEPT: SCYPHOZOA; MEDUSA) | **$400**

$500 | WHAT IS THE INDIAN OCEAN? | **$500**

JEOPARDY!

TOOL TIME

HENRY F. PHILLIPS INVENTED A POPULAR TYPE OF THIS HAND TOOL	**$100**	WHAT IS
IT CAN WEAR DOWN METAL, SHAPE PLASTIC OR BE BAKED IN A CAKE FOR A PRISON INMATE	**$200**	WHAT IS
THIS TYPE OF HAMMER IS NAMED FOR A 2-PRONGED SIDE USED TO PULL NAILS OUT	**$300**	WHAT IS
A BRACE & BIT IS A SIMPLE TYPE OF THIS HAND TOOL	**$400**	WHAT IS
THE CARPENTER & TORPEDO TYPES OF THIS MEASURING TOOL USE BUBBLES AS INDICATORS	**$500**	WHAT ARE

JEOPARDY!™

TOOL TIME

$100	WHAT IS A SCREWDRIVER?	**$100**
$200	WHAT IS A FILE? (ACCEPT: RASP)	**$200**
$300	WHAT IS A CLAW HAMMER?	**$300**
$400	WHAT IS A DRILL?	**$400**
$500	WHAT ARE LEVELS?	**$500**

JEOPARDY!™

STATES' FIGHTS

WEST VIRGINIA BROKE FROM VIRGINIA AFTER THE LEGISLATURE VOTED FOR THIS IN 1861	**$100**	WHAT IS
CALIFORNIA & ARIZONA'S 40-YEAR DISPUTE OVER WATER RIGHTS TO THIS RIVER ENDED IN 1963	**$200**	WHAT IS
MAINE SPLIT FROM THIS STATE IN 1819 IN PROTEST OF HIGH TAXES, POOR ROADS & THE DISTANCE TO THE CAPITAL	**$300**	WHAT IS
IN 1998 NEW YORK & NEW JERSEY MADE THEIR ARGUMENTS BEFORE THE SUPREME COURT OVER THIS HISTORIC ISLAND	**$400**	WHAT IS
IN 1855 MANY MEN FROM THIS SLAVE STATE VOTED IN KANSAS, LEADING TO BLOOD-SHED ALONG THE BORDER	**$500**	WHAT IS

JEOPARDY!™

STATES' FIGHTS

$100 WHAT IS SECESSION (FROM THE UNION)? **$100**

$200 WHAT IS THE COLORADO RIVER? **$200**

$300 WHAT IS MASSACHUSETTS? **$300**

$400 WHAT IS ELLIS ISLAND? **$400**

$500 WHAT IS MISSOURI? **$500**

JEOPARDY!

SPORTS SCORES

ONE STROKE UNDER PAR ON A HOLE IN GOLF IS A BIRDIE; ONE STROKE OVER IS ONE OF THESE	**$100**	WHAT IS
IN FOOTBALL, THE DEFENSE EARNS THIS MANY POINTS BY TACK-LING THE OPPOSING TEAM'S BALL CARRIER IN HIS OWN END ZONE	**$200**	WHAT IS
IN VOLLEYBALL, ONLY THE SIDE WHO DID THIS AT THE BEGINNING OF PLAY CAN SCORE A POINT	**$300**	WHAT IS
IN THE NBA, A SHOT FROM HALF COURT IS WORTH THIS MANY POINTS	**$400**	WHAT IS
IN TOURNAMENT DARTS, IT'S THE MOST POINTS A PLAYER CAN EARN ON ONE THROW; THE MOST FOR ONE TURN IS 180	**$500**	WHAT IS

JEOPARDY!™

SPORTS SCORES

$100   WHAT IS A BOGEY? $100

$200   WHAT IS 2? $200

$300   WHAT IS SERVE? $300

$400   WHAT IS 3? $400

$500   WHAT IS 60? $500

JEOPARDY!

THE "D.T."s

IT'S WHAT YOU HEAR WHEN THE ONE YOU'RE HUNG UP ON HANGS UP ON YOU	**$100**	WHAT IS
IN THE ARMY IT'S A RAPID MARCH OF 180 STEPS A MINUTE	**$200**	WHAT IS
THE NFL's JOE GREENE GOT MEAN FROM THIS POSITION	**$300**	WHAT IS
LONGTIME JOB OF RAWLEY FARNSWORTH, WHO WAS THANKED BY TOM HANKS IN HIS 1994 OSCAR ACCEPTANCE	**$400**	WHAT IS
GROUP OF FLORIDA ISLANDS NAMED FROM THE SPANISH FOR "TURTLES"	**$500**	WHAT ARE

JEOPARDY!

THE "D.T."s

$100 — WHAT IS A DIAL TONE? — $100

$200 — WHAT IS DOUBLE TIME? — $200

$300 — WHAT IS DEFENSIVE TACKLE? — $300

$400 — WHAT IS DRAMA TEACHER? — $400

$500 — WHAT ARE THE DRY TORTUGAS? — $500

JEOPARDY!

VERY MYSTERIOUS

YOU CAN FILL SOME LARGE SHOES IF YOU'RE THIS YETI RELATIVE THAT'S ALSO CALLED A SASQUATCH	**$100**	WHAT IS
THIS INFAMOUS POLYGON SUPPOSEDLY SUCKS UP PLANES & SHIPS WITHOUT A TRACE; DON'T FORGET YOUR SHORTS!	**$200**	WHAT IS
SOME INVESTIGATORS BELIEVE THAT THIS COY LASSIE MIGHT BE A PLESIOSAUR	**$300**	WHO IS
THE EXACT FUNCTION OF THIS MEGALITHIC MONUMENT NEAR SALISBURY, ENGLAND HAS BAFFLED SCHOLARS	**$400**	WHAT IS
THE LAST PROPHECY FROM THE VIRGIN MARY'S APPEARANCE IN THIS PORTUGUESE TOWN BECAME A PAPAL SECRET	**$500**	WHAT IS

JEOPARDY!

VERY MYSTERIOUS

$100	WHAT IS A BIGFOOT?	**$100**
$200	WHAT IS THE BERMUDA TRIANGLE?	**$200**
$300	WHO IS THE LOCH NESS MONSTER? (ACCEPT: NESSIE)	**$300**
$400	WHAT IS STONEHENGE?	**$400**
$500	WHAT IS FATIMA?	**$500**

DOUBLE JEOPARDY!

U.S. CITIES

IN 1965 NASA OPENED ITS $8 MILLION MISSION CONTROL CENTER IN THIS TEXAS CITY	**$200**	WHAT IS
NEIL SIMON'S EUGENE JEROME HAD THE "BLUES" IN THIS MISSISSIPPI CITY	**$400**	WHAT IS
THIS OHIO CITY ON THE OHIO RIVER HAS BEEN DUBBED THE "QUEEN CITY OF THE WEST"	**$600**	WHAT IS
THIS SOUTHERN STATE CAPITAL IS NAMED FOR AN ENGLISH COURTIER	**$800**	WHAT IS
YOU MIGHT STAY AT THE HOTEL DEL CORONADO TO VISIT THIS CITY'S WORLD-FAMOUS ZOO	**$1000**	WHAT IS

DOUBLE JEOPARDY!

U.S. CITIES

$200	WHAT IS HOUSTON?	$200
$400	WHAT IS BILOXI?	$400
$600	WHAT IS CINCINNATI?	$600
$800	WHAT IS RALEIGH (NORTH CAROLINA)?	$800
$1000	WHAT IS SAN DIEGO (CALIFORNIA)?	$1000

DOUBLE JEOPARDY!

ACTS

ACT 2 OF THIS FARCE FINDS ALGERNON MONCRIEFF EARNESTLY PRETENDING TO BE ERNEST WORTHING	**$200**	WHAT IS
ACT 1 OF THIS PLAY INTRODUCES JUROR NO. 8, THE MAN WHO CONVINCES THE OTHER 11 TO RE-EXAMINE THE EVIDENCE	**$400**	WHAT IS
IN ACT 1 OF THIS PLAY, HAPPY COMPLAINS TO BIFF ABOUT THEIR FATHER'S DRIVING	**$600**	WHAT IS
FINALLY IN ACT 2, DR. DYSART SOLVES THE RIDDLE OF THE BLINDED HORSES IN THIS PETER SHAFFER MASTERPIECE	**$800**	WHAT IS
IN ACT 3 OF THIS IONESCO WORK, BERENGER'S LADYLOVE DAISY RUNS OFF TO JOIN A PACK OF HORNED PACHYDERMS	**$1000**	WHAT IS

DOUBLE JEOPARDY!

ACTS

$200 | WHAT IS "THE IMPORTANCE OF BEING EARNEST"? | $200

$400 | WHAT IS "12 ANGRY MEN"? | $400

$600 | WHAT IS "DEATH OF A SALESMAN"? | $600

$800 | WHAT IS "EQUUS"? | $800

$1000 | WHAT IS "RHINOCEROS"? | $1000

DOUBLE JEOPARDY!

FRUIT

ABOUT 50% OF THE U.S. ORANGE CROP IS OF THIS VARIETY THAT SHARES ITS NAME WITH A SPANISH CITY	**$200**	WHAT IS
THE BLACK SEEDS IN A PAPAYA MAY BE GROUND & USED LIKE THIS SPICE	**$400**	WHAT IS
ROLL THIS PERSIAN "FRUIT OF MANY SEEDS" ON THE TABLE & INSERT A STRAW THROUGH THE SKIN TO DRINK ITS JUICE	**$600**	WHAT IS
WHAT AMERICANS CALL THIS IS ACTUALLY AN ORANGE-FLESHED MUSKMELON	**$800**	WHAT IS
THIS FRUIT'S ORIGINS INCLUDE PORTUGAL FOR THE ROCHA, FRANCE FOR THE ANJOU & BELGIUM FOR THE BOSC	**$1000**	WHAT IS

DOUBLE JEOPARDY!

FRUIT

$200	WHAT IS VALENCIA?	**$200**
$400	WHAT IS PEPPER?	**$400**
$600	WHAT IS A POMEGRANATE?	**$600**
$800	WHAT IS A CANTALOUPE?	**$800**
$1000	WHAT IS THE PEAR?	**$1000**

DOUBLE JEOPARDY!

SCULPTURE

THIS ARTIST'S "THE THINKER" WAS ORIGINALLY INTENDED TO CROWN HIS "GATES OF HELL" MONUMENT	$200	WHO IS
ALEXANDER CALDER CALLED THESE CREATIONS "FOUR-DIMENSIONAL DRAWINGS"	$400	WHAT ARE
THIS COUNTRY'S SCULPTOR UNKEI IS RENOWNED FOR HIS WOODEN STATUES CARVED FOR BUDDHIST TEMPLES	$600	WHAT IS
IT FOLLOWS "BAS" IN A TERM FOR SCULPTURE WITH AN IMAGE IS SLIGHTLY RAISED ABOVE A FLAT SURFACE	$800	WHAT IS
A STATUE OF THIS COWBOY PAINTER & SCULPTOR REPRE-SENTS MONTANA IN THE U.S. CAPITOL'S STATUARY HALL	$1000	WHO IS

DOUBLE JEOPARDY!

SCULPTURE

$200	WHO IS AUGUSTE RODIN?	**$200**
$400	WHAT ARE MOBILES?	**$400**
$600	WHAT IS JAPAN?	**$600**
$800	WHAT IS RELIEF?	**$800**
$1000	WHO IS CHARLES MARION RUSSELL?	**$1000**

DOUBLE JEOPARDY!

DEATH SENTENCES

APPROACHING ANOTHER CAR NEAR PASO ROBLES, CA. IN 1955, HIS LAST WORDS WERE "THAT GUY'S GOTTA SEE US"	**$200**	WHO IS
HE ASKED "WHO IS IT?" JUST BEFORE PAT GARRETT SHOT HIM	**$400**	WHO IS
JUST BEFORE THE END, THIS WELSH POET BOASTED, "I'VE HAD 18 STRAIGHT WHISKIES; I THINK THAT'S THE RECORD"	**$600**	WHO IS
SPEAKING OF HIS MISTRESS, THIS ENGLISH KING'S LAST REQUEST WAS "LET NOT POOR NELLY STARVE"	**$800**	WHO IS
JUST BEFORE "DEATH KINDLY STOPPED FOR" HER, THIS POET SIGHED, "I MUST GO IN; THE FOG IS RISING"	**$1000**	WHO IS

DOUBLE JEOPARDY!™

DEATH SENTENCES

$200 WHO IS JAMES DEAN? $200

$400 WHO IS BILLY THE KID? $400

$600 WHO IS DYLAN THOMAS? $600

$800 WHO IS CHARLES II? $800

$1000 WHO IS EMILY DICKINSON? $1000

DOUBLE JEOPARDY!

FILM STARS

AFTER DIVORCING ROBERT WALKER, JENNIFER JONES MARRIED THIS "GONE WITH THE WIND" PRODUCER IN 1949	**$200**	WHO IS
IN "MAGNOLIA" THIS "MISSION: IMPOSSIBLE" STAR RAN A SEMINAR FOR MEN CALLED "SEDUCE AND DESTROY"	**$400**	WHO IS
AN OSCAR WINNER FOR "GOODFELLAS", HE ONCE PLAYED GUITAR FOR JOEY DEE & THE STARLITERS	**$600**	WHO IS
ELLEN MUST HAVE BEEN BURSTYN WITH PRIDE WHEN SHE WON AN OSCAR FOR THIS 1974 ROAD MOVIE	**$800**	WHAT IS
LATER A TALK SHOW HOST FOR CNBC, HE WAS CONSIDERED FOR THE RICHARD DREYFUSS ROLE IN "JAWS"	**$1000**	WHO IS

DOUBLE JEOPARDY!

FILM STARS

$200	WHO IS DAVID O. SELZNICK?	$200
$400	WHO IS TOM CRUISE?	$400
$600	WHO IS JOE PESCI?	$600
$800	WHAT IS "ALICE DOESN'T LIVE HERE ANYMORE"?	$800
$1000	WHO IS CHARLES GRODIN?	$1000

FINAL JEOPARDY!™

BIBLICAL PEOPLE

HE'S THE FIRST PERSON
WHOSE DEATH IS
MENTIONED IN THE
BOOK OF EXODUS

WHO IS

FINAL JEOPARDY!
BIBLICAL PEOPLE

WHO IS JOSEPH?

JEOPARDY!

BODY WORKS

BREATHE EASY—YOUR RIGHT ONE OF THESE HAS 3 LOBES & YOUR LEFT HAS 2	**$100**	WHAT ARE
IT'S THE HINGE-LIKE JOINT THAT ALLOWS THE FOOT TO MOVE UP & DOWN	**$200**	WHAT IS
YOU HAVE 8 OF THESE TEETH, SOME OF WHICH MAY BE BUCK	**$300**	WHAT ARE
THIS PAIR OF TISSUE MASSES THAT CAN CAUSE SNORING LIES ABOVE THE TONSILS IN THE NASAL PASSAGE	**$400**	WHAT ARE
THE ELASTIC TYPE OF THIS CONNECTIVE TISSUE IS FOUND IN THE OUTER PART OF YOUR EAR	**$500**	WHAT IS

JEOPARDY!™

BODY WORKS

$100   WHAT ARE YOUR LUNGS?   **$100**

$200   WHAT IS THE ANKLE?   **$200**

$300   WHAT ARE INCISORS? (ACCEPT: FRONT TEETH)   **$300**

$400   WHAT ARE THE ADENOIDS?   **$400**

$500   WHAT IS CARTILAGE?   **$500**

JEOPARDY!

AUTHORS & THEIR SLEUTHS

HE CREATED MIKE HAMMER & PLAYED THE PART IN THE 1963 FILM "THE GIRL HUNTERS"	**$100**	WHO IS
IN THIS WILKIE COLLINS NOVEL, SERGEANT CUFF SEARCHES FOR THE MISSING TITLE DIAMOND	**$200**	WHAT IS
TITLE OCCUPATION OF CALEB CARR'S DR. LASZLO KREIZLER	**$300**	WHAT IS
THE INITIALS IN THE NAME OF THIS CREATOR OF DETECTIVE ADAM DALGLIESH DON'T STAND FOR "POLICE DEPARTMENT"	**$400**	WHO IS
MICHAEL HARRISON WROTE STORIES FEATURING THIS SLEUTH CREATED BY EDGAR ALLAN POE	**$500**	WHO IS

JEOPARDY!

AUTHORS & THEIR SLEUTHS

$100 WHO IS MICKEY SPILLANE? **$100**

$200 WHAT IS "THE MOONSTONE"? **$200**

$300 WHAT IS AN ALIENIST? **$300**

$400 WHO IS P.D. JAMES? **$400**

$500 WHO IS C. AUGUSTE DUPIN? **$500**

JEOPARDY!

POTENT POTABLES

THE FERMENTED DRINK CALLED PERRY IS THE PEAR-BASED COUNTERPART OF THIS "HARD" APPLE DRINK	**$100**	WHAT IS
A BRAND OF GIN DISTILLED IN LONDON SHARES ITS NAME WITH THESE TOWER OF LONDON GUARDS	**$200**	WHAT ARE
IT'S COFFEE MIXED WITH WHISKEY, SUCH AS JAMESON'S, & TOPPED WITH WHIPPED CREAM	**$300**	WHAT IS
IT'S CALLED STOLI FOR SHORT	**$400**	WHAT IS
TRADER VIC CLAIMED CREDIT FOR INVENTING THIS RUM DRINK & SAID IT WAS NAMED BY A TAHITIAN FRIEND	**$500**	WHAT IS

JEOPARDY!

POTENT POTABLES

$100	WHAT IS CIDER?	**$100**
$200	WHAT ARE BEEFEATERS?	**$200**
$300	WHAT IS IRISH COFFEE?	**$300**
$400	WHAT IS STOLICHNAYA (VODKA)?	**$400**
$500	WHAT IS A MAI TAI?	**$500**

JEOPARDY!

STUPID ANSWERS

SEVENTEEN MAGAZINE SAYS IF YOU CAN'T AFFORD TO BUY A STAIRMASTER & YOUR HOUSE HAS THESE, USE THEM	**$100**	WHAT ARE
NAME OF THE HOTEL & OFFICE COMPLEX WHERE THE WATERGATE BREAK-IN OCCURRED	**$200**	WHAT IS
JESSE JACKSON JR. HAS A MASTERS DEGREE IN THIS FROM THE CHICAGO THEOLOGICAL SEMINARY	**$300**	WHAT IS
2 CIVIL WAR FORTS WERE BUILT ON THIS WESTERN ISLAND OF THE FLORIDA KEYS	**$400**	WHAT IS
IT'S THE CRY OF THE CHACHALACA BIRD OF SOUTH AMERICA	**$500**	WHAT IS

JEOPARDY!

STUPID ANSWERS

$100   WHAT ARE STAIRS?   **$100**

$200   WHAT IS WATERGATE?   **$200**

$300   WHAT IS THEOLOGY?   **$300**

$400   WHAT IS KEY WEST?   **$400**

$500   WHAT IS "CHACHALACA"?   **$500**

JEOPARDY!

AROUND THE WORLD

YOU'LL FIND GREECE'S PARLIAMENT BUILDING ON SYNTAGMA SQUARE IN THIS CAPITAL	**$100**	WHAT IS
THE NAME OF THIS SOUTH AFRICAN PROVINCE MEANS "ACROSS THE VAAL"— THE VAAL RIVER, THAT IS	**$200**	WHAT IS
THIS COUNTRY'S CATHEDRAL OF LEON IS NOTED FOR ITS SOARING SPIRES & STAINED GLASS WINDOWS	**$300**	WHAT IS
THIS CAPITAL OF MALAYSIA LIES AT THE CONFLUENCE OF THE KLANG & GOMBAK RIVERS	**$400**	WHAT IS
THIS CARIBBEAN GROUP OF ISLANDS SHARES ITS NAME WITH AN ANIMAL RESEMBLING AN ALLIGATOR	**$500**	WHAT ARE

JEOPARDY!

AROUND THE WORLD

$100 WHAT IS ATHENS? $100

$200 WHAT IS THE TRANSVAAL? $200

$300 WHAT IS SPAIN? $300

$400 WHAT IS KUALA LUMPUR? $400

$500 WHAT ARE THE CAYMAN ISLANDS? $500

JEOPARDY!

MOVIE DEBUTS

SHE DEBUTED IN A BIT PART AS WOODY ALLEN'S DATE IN "ANNIE HALL" 2 YEARS BEFORE "ALIEN" MADE HER A STAR	**$100**	WHO IS
THIS HALF-SISTER OF COUNTRY SINGER WYNONNA FIRST HIT THE BIG SCREEN IN THE 1992 COMEDY "KUFFS"	**$200**	WHO IS
AT 13 THIS ACTRESS WITH A WEEKDAY IN HER NAME STARRED IN THE 1956 CLASSIC "ROCK, ROCK, ROCK!"	**$300**	WHO IS
THE AL PACINO LEGAL DRAMA ". . . AND JUSTICE FOR ALL" MARKED THE SCREEN DEBUT OF THIS ACTOR, LATER TV's "COACH"	**$400**	WHO IS
THIS SON OF COLLEEN DEWHURST & GEORGE C. SCOTT DEBUTED IN THE 1988 FILM "FIVE CORNERS"	**$500**	WHO IS

JEOPARDY!

MOVIE DEBUTS

$100	WHO IS SIGOURNEY WEAVER?	**$100**
$200	WHO IS ASHLEY JUDD?	**$200**
$300	WHO IS TUESDAY WELD?	**$300**
$400	WHO IS CRAIG T. NELSON?	**$400**
$500	WHO IS CAMPBELL SCOTT?	**$500**

DOUBLE JEOPARDY!

LONG LIVE THE KING

JOHN HANCOCK SIGNED HIS NAME BIG SO "JOHN BULL", INCLUDING THIS KING, COULD READ IT WITHOUT GLASSES	**$200**	WHO IS
WHILE MARRIED TO ISABELLA, THIS 15th CENTURY MONARCH SIRED AT LEAST 2 DAUGHTERS WITH OTHER WOMEN	**$400**	WHO IS
AS HARPSICHORDIST FOR THIS PRUSSIAN KING, CARL PHILIPP EMANUEL BACH OFTEN ACCOMPANIED HIM IN CONCERT	**$600**	WHO IS
IN 1993 HE SUCCEEDED HIS BROTHER BAUDOUIN TO BECOME THE SIXTH KING OF THE BELGIANS	**$800**	WHO IS
PEDRO I, EMPEROR OF BRAZIL, WAS THE SON OF KING JOHN VI OF THIS COUNTRY	**$1000**	WHAT IS

DOUBLE JEOPARDY!

LONG LIVE THE KING

$200	WHO IS GEORGE III?	$200
$400	WHO IS FERDINAND?	$400
$600	WHO IS FREDERICK THE GREAT? (ACCEPT: FREDERICK II)	$600
$800	WHO IS ALBERT (II)?	$800
$1000	WHAT IS PORTUGAL?	$1000

DOUBLE JEOPARDY!

WALL PAINTERS

THIS "DRIPPER", WHO PAINTED ON THE FLOOR, WAS A STUDENT OF MISSOURI MURALIST THOMAS HART BENTON	**$200**	WHO IS
AT AGE 4 IN GUANAJUATO, MEXICO, HE WAS ALREADY DRAWING ON THE WALLS	**$400**	WHO IS
IN 1892 THE WORLD'S COLUMBIAN EXPO IN CHICAGO HIRED THIS WOMAN IMPRESSIONIST TO PAINT A MURAL	**$600**	WHO IS
THIS "THIRD OF MAY" ARTIST COVERED THE WALLS OF HIS COUNTRY HOUSE IN GROTESQUE PAINTINGS	**$800**	WHO IS
STUART DAVIS' MURAL FOR THIS ROOM IN ROCKEFELLER CENTER WAS TITLED "MURAL (MEN WITHOUT WOMEN)"	**$1000**	WHAT IS

DOUBLE JEOPARDY!

WALL PAINTERS

$200	WHO IS JACKSON POLLOCK?	**$200**
$400	WHO IS DIEGO RIVERA?	**$400**
$600	WHO IS MARY CASSATT?	**$600**
$800	WHO IS FRANCISCO GOYA?	**$800**
$1000	WHAT IS THE MEN'S ROOM?	**$1000**

DOUBLE JEOPARDY!

MEMORABLE TV

SHOW ON WHICH YOU'D SEE CESAR ROMERO AS THE JOKER & DAVID WAYNE AS THE MAD HATTER	**$200**	WHAT IS
SHOW THAT GAVE US THE CATCH PHRASES "YOU BET YOUR BIPPY" & "HERE COME DE JUDGE"	**$400**	WHAT IS
MANY THOUGHT THE REAL STAR OF THIS '80s SERIES WAS A CAR CALLED THE GENERAL LEE	**$600**	WHAT IS
DR. KILDARE & THIS VINCE EDWARDS DOCTOR BEGAN PRACTICING ON TV IN 1961 & BOTH LEFT IN 1966	**$800**	WHO IS
HE SMOLDERED AS LANCE CUMSON ON "FALCON CREST"	**$1000**	WHO IS

DOUBLE JEOPARDY!

MEMORABLE TV

$200	WHAT IS "BATMAN"?	**$200**
$400	WHAT IS "(ROWAN & MARTIN'S) LAUGH-IN"?	**$400**
$600	WHAT IS "THE DUKES OF HAZZARD"?	**$600**
$800	WHO IS BEN CASEY?	**$800**
$1000	WHO IS LORENZO LAMAS?	**$1000**

DOUBLE JEOPARDY!

AT GREAT LENGTHS

TYPE OF "MILE" EQUAL TO 1 KNOT OR 1 MEAN MINUTE OF ARC ON THE MERIDIAN	**$200**	WHAT IS
THIS DISTANCE USED IN ASTRONOMY IS ABBREVIATED pc & IS EQUAL TO 19.2 TRILLION MILES	**$400**	WHAT IS
USED IN TAKING SOUNDINGS, IT EQUALS EXACTLY 6 FEET	**$600**	WHAT IS
IN THE 1968 OLYMPICS HE LONG-JUMPED AN AMAZING 29 FEET, 2 1/2 INCHES	**$800**	WHO IS
IT USUALLY EQUALED 3 MILES, SO THOSE FABLED BOOTS WOULD COVER 21 MILES	**$1000**	WHAT IS

DOUBLE JEOPARDY!

AT GREAT LENGTHS

$200	WHAT IS A NAUTICAL MILE?	**$200**
$400	WHAT IS A PARSEC?	**$400**
$600	WHAT IS A FATHOM?	**$600**
$800	WHO IS BOB BEAMON?	**$800**
$1000	WHAT IS A LEAGUE?	**$1000**

DOUBLE JEOPARDY!

OFFICIAL STATE SEALS

THIS STATE'S SEAL FEATURES 2 CORNU-COPIAS, ONE CON-TAINING A COUPLE OF SPUDS	**$200**	WHAT IS
THE REVERSE SIDE OF ITS SEAL CONTAINS THE 6 FLAGS OF THE NATIONS THAT ONCE RULED IT	**$400**	WHAT IS
NEW JERSEY'S SEAL SHOWS 3 PLOWS ON A SHIELD HELD BY LIBERTY & THIS ROMAN GODDESS OF AGRICULTURE	**$600**	WHO IS
ITS SEAL WAS CREATED IN 1905 FOR A PRO-POSED STATE OF SEQUOYAH ENCOM-PASSING 5 INDIAN REPUBLICS	**$800**	WHAT IS
A SEMINOLE WOMAN CAN BE SEEN ON ITS SEAL SPREADING FLOWERS ALONG THE SHORE	**$1000**	WHAT IS

DOUBLE JEOPARDY!

OFFICIAL STATE SEALS

$200 — WHAT IS IDAHO? — $200

$400 — WHAT IS TEXAS? — $400

$600 — WHO IS CERES? — $600

$800 — WHAT IS OKLAHOMA? — $800

$1000 — WHAT IS FLORIDA? — $1000

DOUBLE JEOPARDY!

HEARD IN THE '80s

IN "SUDDEN IMPACT", CLINT EASTWOOD TOLD A BAD GUY, "GO AHEAD", DO THIS	**$200**	WHAT IS
"BORKING", CLOSE SCRUTINY, WAS HEARD AFTER ROBERT BORK'S FAILED NOMINATION TO THIS BODY	**$400**	WHAT IS
MARGARET THATCHER SAID OF THIS SOVIET LEADER, "WE CAN DO BUSINESS TOGETHER"	**$600**	WHO IS
AFTER BEING SHOT, RONALD REAGAN QUOTED JACK DEMPSEY'S "I FORGOT TO" DO THIS	**$800**	WHAT IS
IN 1986 DAN RATHER WAS ASSAULTED BY THUGS CALLING HIM "KENNETH" & ASKING THIS	**$1000**	WHAT IS

DOUBLE JEOPARDY!

HEARD IN THE '80s

$200 | WHAT IS "MAKE MY DAY"? | **$200**

$400 | WHAT IS THE U.S. SUPREME COURT? | **$400**

$600 | WHO IS MIKHAIL GORBACHEV? | **$600**

$800 | WHAT IS DUCK? | **$800**

$1000 | (WHAT IS) WHAT'S THE FREQUENCY? | **$1000**

FINAL JEOPARDY!

CLASSICAL COMPOSERS

ONE OF HIS MOST FAMOUS
WORKS HAD ITS PREMIERE
ON A BARGE IN 1717

WHO IS

FINAL JEOPARDY!

CLASSICAL COMPOSERS

WHO IS
GEORGE FRIDERIC HANDEL?

JEOPARDY!

STATE CAPITALS

THIS NEW YORK CAPITAL WAS ONCE KNOWN AS BEVERWYCK	**$100**	WHAT IS
IN 1982 ALASKANS REJECTED A PROPOSAL THAT WOULD HAVE MADE WILLOW THE CAPITAL INSTEAD OF THIS CITY	**$200**	WHAT IS
IN HOPES THAT GERMANY WOULD HELP FINANCE ITS RAILROAD, NORTH DAKOTA NAMED ITS CAPITAL THIS	**$300**	WHAT IS
BUILT IN 1610, THE SPANISH PALACE OF GOVERNORS IN THIS SOUTHWEST CAPITAL IS NOW A MUSEUM	**$400**	WHAT IS
IT'S "THE BIRTHPLACE OF DIXIE"	**$500**	WHAT IS

JEOPARDY!

STATE CAPITALS

$100 — WHAT IS ALBANY? — $100

$200 — WHAT IS JUNEAU? — $200

$300 — WHAT IS BISMARCK? — $300

$400 — WHAT IS SANTA FE (NEW MEXICO)? — $400

$500 — WHAT IS MONTGOMERY (ALABAMA)? — $500

JEOPARDY!

COW-ARDICE

LAST NAME OF THE WOMAN WHOSE COW ALLEGEDLY STARTED THE GREAT CHICAGO FIRE	**$100**	WHAT IS
MILKY-WHITE WAS THE NAME OF THE COW THAT THIS FICTIONAL KID SOLD FOR BEANS	**$200**	WHO IS
ELSIE, THIS DAIRY COMPANY'S COW SYMBOL, FIRST APPEARED LIVE AT THE 1939 WORLD'S FAIR	**$300**	WHAT IS
MRS. WIGGINS IS THE COW BUDDY OF FREDDY, A HEROIC ONE OF THESE ANIMALS IN BOOKS BY WALTER R. BROOKS	**$400**	WHAT IS
ANCIENT PEOPLE WHOSE GODDESS HATHOR HAD THE HEAD OF A COW	**$500**	WHO ARE

237

JEOPARDY!™

COW-ARDICE

$100   WHAT IS O'LEARY?   **$100**

$200   WHO IS JACK?   **$200**

$300   WHAT IS BORDEN?   **$300**

$400   WHAT IS A PIG?   **$400**

$500   WHO ARE THE EGYPTIANS?   **$500**

JEOPARDY!™

MEDICAL KNOWLEDGE

IT'S BEEN JOKINGLY SAID OF THIS SPECIALTY THAT TREATS SKIN DISORDERS, "1,000 CONDITIONS; 2 CREAMS"	**$100**	WHAT IS
IN 1816 FRENCH PHYSICIAN RENE LAENNEC INVENTED THIS DEVICE USED TO LISTEN TO THE HEART & LUNGS	**$200**	WHAT IS
IN 1895 THIS SCIENTIST COULD SEE RIGHT THROUGH HIS WIFE; HE TOOK X-RAYS OF HER HAND	**$300**	WHO IS
NAMED FOR A PHYSICIAN BORN AROUND 460 B.C., IT INCLUDES A PLEDGE NOT TO SEDUCE A PATIENT'S SLAVES	**$400**	WHAT IS
THIS SYMBOL OF THE PHYSICIAN IS DERIVED FROM THE WAND OF AESCULAPIUS, THE GOD OF MEDICINE	**$500**	WHAT IS

JEOPARDY!™

MEDICAL KNOWLEDGE

$100 — WHAT IS DERMATOLOGY? — $100

$200 — WHAT IS A STETHOSCOPE? — $200

$300 — WHO IS WILHELM ROENTGEN? — $300

$400 — WHAT IS THE HIPPOCRATIC OATH? — $400

$500 — WHAT IS THE CADUCEUS? — $500

JEOPARDY!

CHARLIE PARKER

Clue	Value	Response
PARKER WAS SELF-TAUGHT ON THIS MUSICAL INSTRUMENT HE GOT FROM HIS MOTHER AT AGE 11	**$100**	WHAT IS
FOREST WHITAKER PLAYED THE LEAD ROLE IN THIS DIRECTOR'S 1988 FILM "BIRD"	**$200**	WHO IS
DIZZY GILLESPIE, PARKER & OTHERS DEVELOPED THIS NEW STYLE OF JAZZ AT MINTON'S PLAYHOUSE, A NYC NIGHTCLUB	**$300**	WHAT IS
THIS MUSICAL BIRD "STUDY" BY PARKER WAS BASED ON THE CHORD PROGRESSIONS OF "HOW HIGH THE MOON"	**$400**	WHAT IS
DUE TO PARKER'S PROMINENCE, THIS LEADING NEW YORK CITY JAZZ CLUB WAS NAMED FOR HIM	**$500**	WHAT IS

JEOPARDY!™

CHARLIE PARKER

$100   WHAT IS THE (ALTO) SAXOPHONE? $100

$200   WHO IS CLINT EASTWOOD? $200

$300   WHAT IS BEBOP? (ACCEPT: BOP) $300

$400   WHAT IS "ORNITHOLOGY"? $400

$500   WHAT IS BIRDLAND? $500

JEOPARDY!™

"IN" & "OUT" PHRASES

A COOKING SITUATION THAT'S GONE FROM BAD TO WORSE	**$100**	WHAT IS
TO BE OUT OF FAVOR TEMPORARILY, AS WHEN MR. DARLING IN "PETER PAN" WAS EXILED TO NANA'S KENNEL	**$200**	WHAT IS
VISUAL CLICHE THAT'S THE OPPOSITE OF "ABSENCE MAKES THE HEART GROW FONDER"	**$300**	WHAT IS
LADY MACBETH'S 3-WORD LAMENT WHILE SLEEPWALKING, IT PRECEDES "OUT, I SAY!"	**$400**	WHAT IS
THIS LATIN PHRASE FROM HORACE MEANS "IN THE MIDST OF THINGS", ESPECIALLY OF A STORY	**$500**	WHAT IS

JEOPARDY!™

"IN" & "OUT" PHRASES

$100 WHAT IS "OUT OF THE FRYING PAN AND INTO THE FIRE"? **$100**

$200 WHAT IS "(TO BE) IN THE DOGHOUSE"? **$200**

$300 WHAT IS "OUT OF SIGHT, OUT OF MIND"? **$300**

$400 WHAT IS "OUT, DAMNED SPOT"? **$400**

$500 WHAT IS "IN MEDIAS RES"? **$500**

JEOPARDY!

WORK, WORK, WORK

SPECIFIC TERM FOR AN INVESTIGATOR OF INSURANCE CLAIMS	**$100**	WHAT IS
IN L.A. COUNTY JAILS, "INMATE WORKER" HAS REPLACED THIS TERM THAT'S A SYNONYM FOR "RELIABLE"	**$200**	WHAT IS
A CARNIVAL WORKER WHOM CUSTOMERS TRY TO DUNK, OR A LARRY HARMON CLOWN	**$300**	WHAT IS
TYPE OF "BANKER" WHO BUYS ISSUES OF STOCK & RESELLS THEM TO THE PUBLIC	**$400**	WHAT IS
BUSINESS OF THE LOIZEAUX FAMILY, KNOWN FOR THEIR WORK ON THE PRUITT-IGOE HOUSING PROJECT & THE SANDS HOTEL	**$500**	WHAT IS

JEOPARDY!™

WORK, WORK, WORK

$100 — WHAT IS AN ADJUSTER? — $100

$200 — WHAT IS TRUSTY? — $200

$300 — WHAT IS A BOZO? — $300

$400 — WHAT IS AN INVESTMENT BANKER? — $400

$500 — WHAT IS DEMOLITION? — $500

DOUBLE JEOPARDY!

LINES FROM LONGFELLOW

"FROM THE WATERFALL HE NAMED HER" THIS, MEANING "LAUGHING WATER"	**$200**	WHAT IS
DISTINGUISHING FEATURE OF THE GIRL WHO WAS VERY, VERY GOOD BUT "WHEN SHE WAS BAD SHE WAS HORRID"	**$400**	WHAT IS
THE 1874 BOOK OF "TALES FROM" HERE INCLUDES "PAUL REVERE'S RIDE" & THE LINE "SHIPS THAT PASS IN THE NIGHT"	**$600**	WHAT IS
THEY'RE WHAT WE CAN "LEAVE BEHIND US . . . ON THE SANDS OF TIME"	**$800**	WHAT ARE
"SANTA FILOMENA", ABOUT THIS WOMAN, STATES: "A LADY WITH A LAMP SHALL STAND IN THE GREAT HISTORY OF THE LAND"	**$1000**	WHO IS

DOUBLE JEOPARDY!

LINES FROM LONGFELLOW

$200	WHAT IS MINNEHAHA?	$200
$400	WHAT IS A (LITTLE) CURL?	$400
$600	WHAT IS "A WAYSIDE INN"?	$600
$800	WHAT ARE FOOTPRINTS?	$800
$1000	WHO IS FLORENCE NIGHTINGALE?	$1000

DOUBLE JEOPARDY!

HISTORIC FIGURES

IN 1930 HE LED A MARCH TO THE SEA TO COLLECT SALT TO PROTEST A MONOPOLY BY THE GOVERNMENT OF INDIA	**$200**	WHO IS
IN 1979 THIS VICE-PREMIER BECAME THE FIRST TOP COMMUNIST LEADER FROM CHINA TO VISIT THE U.S.	**$400**	WHO IS
IN AN 1880 LETTER, QUEEN VICTORIA REFERRED TO THIS SUCCESSOR OF DISRAELI AS A "HALF-MAD FIRE-BRAND"	**$600**	WHO IS
THE EAGLE ON IRAQ'S COAT OF ARMS IS ASSOCIATED WITH THIS 12th CENTURY MUSLIM WARRIOR	**$800**	WHO IS
A LITTLE BIRDIE "PTOLD" ME: AFTER ALEXANDER THE GREAT'S DEATH, THIS GENERAL TOOK CONTROL OF EGYPT	**$1000**	WHO IS

249

DOUBLE JEOPARDY!

HISTORIC FIGURES

$200	WHO IS MOHANDAS (MAHATMA) GANDHI?	**$200**
$400	WHO IS DENG XIAOPING?	**$400**
$600	WHO IS WILLIAM GLADSTONE?	**$600**
$800	WHO IS SALADIN?	**$800**
$1000	WHO IS PTOLEMY(I)?	**$1000**

DOUBLE JEOPARDY!

POP MUSIC PEOPLE

Clue	Value	Response
THE SYMBOL THIS SINGER USED TO REPLACE HIS NAME WAS REFERRED TO AS A "GLYPH"	**$200**	WHO IS
SHE'S "THE QUEEN OF SOUL" &, ACCORDING TO THE KENNEDY CENTER HONORS, "AN ICON OF CONTEMPORARY POP MUSIC"	**$400**	WHO IS
THIS FORMER BOOMTOWN RATS LEADER WAS KNIGHTED FOR HIS FAMINE-RELIEF WORK	**$600**	WHO IS
THIS COUNTRY SUPERSTAR WAS BORN ON AUGUST 28, 1982	**$800**	WHO IS
WHEN HE & HIS WIFE JANE DIVORCED, WE DON'T KNOW IF SHE TOLD HIM, "DON'T COME AROUND HERE NO MORE"	**$1000**	WHO IS

DOUBLE JEOPARDY!

POP MUSIC PEOPLE

$200	WHO IS (THE ARTIST FORMERLY KNOWN AS) PRINCE?	**$200**
$400	WHO IS ARETHA FRANKLIN?	**$400**
$600	WHO IS (SIR) BOB GELDOF?	**$600**
$800	WHO IS LEANN RIMES?	**$800**
$1000	WHO IS TOM PETTY?	**$1000**

DOUBLE JEOPARDY!

INVESTMENT ADVICE

Clue	Value	Response
CONSIDER THE "WHOLE LIFE" TYPE OF THIS, UNLESS YOU'RE PLANNING TO DIE SOON	**$200**	WHAT IS
TO MINIMIZE YOUR RISK, BUY THESE "COLORFUL" STOCKS IN ESTABLISHED, RELIABLE COMPANIES	**$400**	WHAT ARE
DON'T BLOW YOUR MONEY ON RAP CDs (COMPACT DISCS), PUT IT IN ONE OF THESE BANK CDs	**$600**	WHAT IS
THIS NEW TYPE OF IRA NAMED FOR A SENATOR ALLOWS TAX-FREE WITHDRAWALS WHEN YOU'RE IN YOUR 60s	**$800**	WHAT IS
IF BUYING CORPORATE OR MUNICIPAL BONDS, YOU SHOULD KNOW THIS IS MOODY'S HIGHEST RATING	**$1000**	WHAT IS

DOUBLE JEOPARDY!

INVESTMENT ADVICE

$200	WHAT IS (LIFE) INSURANCE?	**$200**
$400	WHAT ARE BLUE CHIP (STOCKS)?	**$400**
$600	WHAT IS A CERTIFICATE OF DEPOSIT?	**$600**
$800	WHAT IS A ROTH IRA?	**$800**
$1000	WHAT IS AAA?	**$1000**

DOUBLE JEOPARDY!

THE ANIMAL KINGDOM

YOU CAN'T CALL SNAKES SPINELESS: THEY MAY HAVE OVER 300 OF THESE BONES, COMPARED TO HUMANS' 33	**$200**	WHAT ARE
THIS TYPE OF CATFISH CAN GENERATE A 450-VOLT SHOCK, LESS THAN THE "EEL" OF THE SAME NAME	**$400**	WHAT IS
THE BARN SPECIES OF THIS BIRD IS SOMETIMES CALLED MONKEY-FACED DUE TO ITS SIMIAN FEATURES	**$600**	WHAT IS
AN ENDANGERED NORTH AFRICAN DEER IS CALLED THIS, LIKE AN "APE" FOUND ON GIBRALTAR	**$800**	WHAT IS
YOUNG RABBITS ARE BUNNIES; YOUNG ONES OF THESE ARE LEVERETS	**$1000**	WHAT ARE

DOUBLE JEOPARDY!

THE ANIMAL KINGDOM

$200 — WHAT ARE VERTEBRAE? (ACCEPT: BACKBONES) — **$200**

$400 — WHAT IS ELECTRIC? — **$400**

$600 — WHAT IS THE OWL? — **$600**

$800 — WHAT IS BARBARY (DEER OR STAG)? — **$800**

$1000 — WHAT ARE HARES? — **$1000**

DOUBLE JEOPARDY!

GET "BACK"

SWIMMERS DO IT FACE UP WITH THEIR ARMS MOVING ALTERNATELY OVER THEIR HEADS	**$200**	WHAT IS
THIS GAME PLAYED ON A BOARD WITH 24 SPEAR-SHAPED POINTS MAY HAVE EVOLVED FROM PARCHEESI	**$400**	WHAT IS
USING THIS TECHNIQUE, A PERSON CAN POSSIBLY CONTROL HIS OWN BLOOD PRESSURE & BODY TEMPERATURE	**$600**	WHAT IS
IT'S A VERY VOCAL SEA CREATURE WITH A CHARACTERISTIC ARCH OF THE BODY WHEN LEAPING	**$800**	WHAT IS
THEY'RE FAYETTEVILLE'S FAVORITE COLLEGE FOOTBALL TEAM	**$1000**	WHAT ARE

257

DOUBLE JEOPARDY!

GET "BACK"

$200	WHAT IS THE BACKSTROKE? (ACCEPT: BACKCRAWL)	$200
$400	WHAT IS BACKGAMMON?	$400
$600	WHAT IS BIOFEEDBACK?	$600
$800	WHAT IS A HUMPBACK WHALE?	$800
$1000	WHAT ARE THE (ARKANSAS) RAZORBACKS?	$1000

FINAL JEOPARDY!

POPULAR PSYCHOLOGY

THIS 1973 BOOK &
SUBSEQUENT TV MOVIE
POPULARIZED THE
STUDY OF MULTIPLE
PERSONALITY DISORDER

WHAT IS

FINAL JEOPARDY!

POPULAR PSYCHOLOGY

WHAT IS "SYBIL"?

JEOPARDY!

THE HIMALAYAS

Clue	Value	Response
IN SANSKRIT "HIMALAYA" MEANS "HOME OF" THIS SUBSTANCE	**$100**	WHAT IS
AN ICE CAVE AT OVER 10,000 FEET NEAR GANGOTRI IN THE HIMALAYAS IS THE SOURCE OF THIS SACRED INDIAN RIVER	**$200**	WHAT IS
THIS SHAGGY-HAIRED BEAST OF TIBET IS OFTEN CALLED THE GRUNTING OX BECAUSE OF THE SOUND IT MAKES	**$300**	WHAT IS
SOME HAVE SUGGESTED THAT THIS MYTHICAL HIMALAYAN CREATURE IS A PRE-HUMAN PRIMATE	**$400**	WHAT IS
THESE NEPALESE PEOPLE ARE MUCH SOUGHT AFTER AS PORTERS FOR HIMALAYAN CLIMBING EXPEDITIONS	**$500**	WHAT ARE

JEOPARDY!

THE HIMALAYAS

$100 — WHAT IS SNOW? — $100

$200 — WHAT IS THE GANGES RIVER? (ACCEPT: BHAGIRATHI) — $200

$300 — WHAT IS THE YAK? — $300

$400 — WHAT IS THE ABOMINABLE SNOWMAN? (ACCEPT: YETI) — $400

$500 — WHAT ARE THE SHERPAS? — $500

JEOPARDY!

GENERAL KNOWLEDGE

THE HOUSES OF LANCASTER & YORK USED DIFFERENT-COLORED TYPES OF THESE FLOWERS AS THEIR SYMBOLS	**$100**	WHAT ARE
NATIVE AMERICANS GREW THESE BEANS WITH CORN & AT HARVEST TIME COMBINED THEM INTO "M'SICKQUATASH"	**$200**	WHAT ARE
HE WAS THICK-SKULLED, HEAVY-BROWED, ABOUT 5 FEET TALL & NAMED FOR A PLACE IN GERMANY	**$300**	WHO IS
THE NUMBER OF DIFFERENT HEXAGRAMS IN THE I CHING, OR THE NUMBER OF SQUARES ON A CHECKERBOARD	**$400**	WHAT IS
2-WORD TERM FOR THE KEY WEEKDAY OF THE PRIMARY SEASON, LIKE MARCH 7, 2000	**$500**	WHAT IS

JEOPARDY!™

GENERAL KNOWLEDGE

$100   WHAT ARE ROSES?   **$100**

$200   WHAT ARE LIMA BEANS?   **$200**

$300   WHO IS NEANDERTHAL MAN?   **$300**

$400   WHAT IS 64?   **$400**

$500   WHAT IS SUPER TUESDAY?   **$500**

JEOPARDY!™

WISCON-SIN

ON AUGUST 9, 1966 THE MILWAUKEE HQ OF THIS VENERABLE CIVIL RIGHTS ORGANIZATION WAS BOMBED	**$100**	WHAT IS
IN 1970 ACTIVISTS BLEW UP THE ARMY MATHEMATICS RESEARCH CENTER AT THE UNIVERSITY OF WISCONSIN IN THIS CITY	**$200**	WHAT IS
THIS CANNIBALISTIC SERIAL KILLER WAS SLAIN IN A WISCONSIN PRISON IN 1994	**$300**	WHO IS
IN A 1912 ASSASSI-NATION ATTEMPT, TEDDY ROOSEVELT WAS SAVED WHEN THE BULLET HIT THIS CASE IN HIS POCKET	**$400**	WHAT IS
A BOMB AT CAMPAIGN HQ IN MADISON DIDN'T STOP THE 1994 REELECTION OF TOMMY THOMPSON TO THIS OFFICE	**$500**	WHAT IS

JEOPARDY!™

WISCON-SIN

$100 WHAT IS THE NAACP? **$100**

$200 WHAT IS MADISON? **$200**

$300 WHO IS JEFFREY DAHMER? **$300**

$400 WHAT IS HIS GLASSES CASE? **$400**

$500 WHAT IS GOVERNOR? **$500**

JEOPARDY!

VOCALISTS

HE SANG "SONG SUNG BLUE" & "FOREVER IN BLUE JEANS"	**$100**	WHO IS
"YOU'RE SO VAIN" WAS A BESTSELLER FOR THIS PUBLISHING HEIRESS	**$200**	WHO IS
ONETIME COMMODORE WHO GAVE US "SAY YOU, SAY ME"	**$300**	WHO IS
HER LESS-THAN-TITANIC HITS INCLUDE "MISLED" & "NOTHING BROKEN BUT MY HEART"	**$400**	WHO IS
SHE SANG THE IMPASSIONED "I'M THE ONLY ONE" & "COME TO MY WINDOW"	**$500**	WHO IS

JEOPARDY!

VOCALISTS

$100   WHO IS NEIL DIAMOND?   **$100**

$200   WHO IS CARLY SIMON?   **$200**

$300   WHO IS LIONEL RICHIE?   **$300**

$400   WHO IS CELINE DION?   **$400**

$500   WHO IS MELISSA ETHERIDGE?   **$500**

JEOPARDY!

THE MALE OF THE SPECIES

THIS BOY'S NAME IS GIVEN TO ANY MALE HOUSECAT	**$100**	WHAT IS
A HEN'S MATE, OR ANY BIRD THAT SETTLES ON A PERCH	**$200**	WHAT IS
THIS TERM FOR A MALE DUCK ALSO REFERS TO AN OLD TYPE OF CANNON	**$300**	WHAT IS
DOE, A RABBIT, A FEMALE RABBIT, & THIS, A MALE	**$400**	WHAT IS
WHEN MALE BADGERS & PIGS GET TOGETHER, THE FEMALES THINK THEY'RE A BUNCH OF THESE	**$500**	WHAT ARE

JEOPARDY!

THE MALE OF THE SPECIES

$100 — WHAT IS A TOM (CAT)? — $100

$200 — WHAT IS A ROOSTER? — $200

$300 — WHAT IS A DRAKE? — $300

$400 — WHAT IS A BUCK? — $400

$500 — WHAT ARE BOARS? — $500

JEOPARDY!

VILIFICATION

ROSSINI SAID OF THIS "RING" LEADER, "HE HAS LOVELY MOMENTS BUT AWFUL QUARTERS OF AN HOUR"	**$100**	WHO IS
MARIO PUZO WROTE THAT ONE OF THESE MEN "WITH HIS BRIEF-CASE CAN STEAL MORE THAN A HUNDRED MEN WITH GUNS"	**$200**	WHAT IS
IN 1984 BARBARA BUSH SAID OF THIS VICE PRESIDENTIAL NOMINEE, "IT RHYMES WITH RICH", BUT LATER APOLOGIZED	**$300**	WHO IS
DOROTHY PARKER'S COMMENT ON THIS ACTRESS, "SHE RUNS THE GAMUT OF EMOTIONS FROM A TO B", WAS A JOKE	**$400**	WHO IS
HERMAN MANKIEWICZ SAID OF THIS DIRECTOR, "THERE, BUT FOR THE GRACE OF GOD, GOES GOD"	**$500**	WHO IS

JEOPARDY!

VILIFICATION

$100	WHO IS RICHARD WAGNER?	**$100**
$200	WHAT IS A LAWYER?	**$200**
$300	WHO IS GERALDINE FERRARO?	**$300**
$400	WHO IS KATHARINE HEPBURN?	**$400**
$500	WHO IS ORSON WELLES?	**$500**

DOUBLE JEOPARDY!

CONFEDERATES

THIS AUTHOR & STEAMBOAT PILOT'S CIVIL WAR EXPERIENCE WAS SERVING ABOUT A MONTH IN THE MISSOURI MILITIA	**$200**	WHO IS
THIS NICKNAME THAT GENERAL BARNARD BEE GAVE THOMAS JACKSON MAY HAVE BEEN AN INSULT	**$400**	WHAT IS
PIERRE G.T. BEAURE-GARD WAS KNOWN AS "THE LITTLE" THIS FROM HIS ADMIRATION OF THE FRENCH LEADER	**$600**	WHAT IS
GENERAL JOSEPH JOHNSTON'S ARRIVAL HELPED THE SOUTH WIN THE JULY 1861 FIRST BATTLE OF THIS VIRGINIA PLACE	**$800**	WHAT IS
HE NEVER FORGAVE LEE FOR HAVING HIM SEND HIS MEN ON THAT DOOMED CHARGE AT GETTYSBURG	**$1000**	WHO IS

DOUBLE JEOPARDY!

CONFEDERATES

$200	WHO IS MARK TWAIN? (ACCEPT: SAMUEL CLEMENS)	**$200**
$400	WHAT IS STONEWALL?	**$400**
$600	WHAT IS NAPOLEON?	**$600**
$800	WHAT IS BULL RUN? (ACCEPT: MANASSAS)	**$800**
$1000	WHO IS GEORGE EDWARD PICKETT?	**$1000**

DOUBLE JEOPARDY!

MEDICAL MEN

IN THE 1980s ROBERT GALLO IDENTIFIED THIS AIDS-CAUSING VIRUS BUT CALLED IT HTLV	**$200**	WHAT IS
THIS NOVELIST & MEDICAL SCHOOL GRADUATE (HARVARD '69) CREATED THE TV SHOW "ER"	**$400**	WHO IS
STANLEY PRUSINER'S THEORY OF PRIONS MAY EXPLAIN THIS DISEASE ALSO CALLED BOVINE SPONGIFORM ENCEPHALOPATHY	**$600**	WHAT IS
A TYPE OF CHOREA, A NERVE DISEASE, IS NAMED FOR THIS PHYSICIAN WHO DIED IN 1916	**$800**	WHO IS
THIS ENGLISH DIS-COVERER OF BLOOD CIRCULATION STUDIED AT PADUA WITH THE GREAT ANATOMIST AQUAPENDENTE	**$1000**	WHO IS

DOUBLE JEOPARDY!

MEDICAL MEN

$200   WHAT IS HIV?   **$200**

$400   WHO IS MICHAEL CRICHTON?   **$400**

$600   WHAT IS MAD COW DISEASE?   **$600**

$800   WHO IS GEORGE S. HUNTINGTON?   **$800**

$1000   WHO IS WILLIAM HARVEY?   **$1000**

DOUBLE JEOPARDY!

THE "BIG" SCREEN

IN IT, PAUL REUBENS' ALTER EGO JOINS THE CIRCUS	**$200**	WHAT IS
IT'S THE 1970 DUSTIN HOFFMAN FILM WITH THE LINE "IT'S A GOOD DAY TO DIE"	**$400**	WHAT IS
HUMPHREY BOGART PLAYED PHILIP MARLOWE IN THIS 1946 FILM	**$600**	WHAT IS
LEE MARVIN & MARK HAMILL STARRED IN THIS 1980 SAM FULLER FILM FULL OF WWII STORIES	**$800**	WHAT IS
THIS COEN BROTHERS FILM STARRING JEFF BRIDGES FEATURED JOHN TURTURRO AS AN EGOMANIACAL BOWLER	**$1000**	WHAT IS

DOUBLE JEOPARDY!

THE "BIG" SCREEN

$200	WHAT IS "BIG TOP PEE WEE"?	**$200**
$400	WHAT IS "LITTLE BIG MAN"?	**$400**
$600	WHAT IS "THE BIG SLEEP"?	**$600**
$800	WHAT IS "THE BIG RED ONE"?	**$800**
$1000	WHAT IS "THE BIG LEBOWSKI"?	**$1000**

DOUBLE JEOPARDY!

STREET SMARTS

IT'S SYNONYMOUS WITH THE STOCK MARKET	**$200**	WHAT IS
WHILE BRITISH PRIME MINISTER, MARGARET THATCHER HAD GATES PUT UP ON THE WHITEHALL END OF THIS STREET	**$400**	WHAT IS
WE WONDER IF GENERAL GRANT WAS SINGING THE BLUES WHEN HE SET UP HEADQUARTERS ON THIS MEMPHIS STREET	**$600**	WHAT IS
STREETS IN THIS CITY INCLUDE RALPH DAVID ABERNATHY BOULEVARD & COCA COLA PLACE	**$800**	WHAT IS
SAN FRANCISCO THROUGHFARE KNOWN AS "THE CROOKEDEST STREET IN THE WORLD"	**$1000**	WHAT IS

DOUBLE JEOPARDY!

STREET SMARTS

$200	WHAT IS WALL STREET?	**$200**
$400	WHAT IS DOWNING STREET?	**$400**
$600	WHAT IS BEALE STREET?	**$600**
$800	WHAT IS ATLANTA?	**$800**
$1000	WHAT IS LOMBARD STREET?	**$1000**

DOUBLE JEOPARDY!

LAZYBONES

TRADEMARK NAME OF A SHOE INDICATING IT'S MEANT FOR THOSE TOO LAZY TO LACE & TIE	**$200**	WHAT IS
IN AN AESOP FABLE, THESE INSECTS LAUGH AT A HUNGRY CICADA WHO GOOFED OFF ALL SUMMER	**$400**	WHAT ARE
PROVERBIALLY, "THE DEVIL FINDS WORK FOR" THESE "TO DO"	**$600**	WHAT ARE
IT'S RICHARD LINK-LATER'S 1991 FILM ABOUT THE SUB-CULTURE OF AUSTIN, TEXAS DROPOUTS & HANGERS-OUT	**$800**	WHAT IS
IN THE 1948 CAMPAIGN, IT WAS TRUMAN'S FAVORITE ADJECTIVE FOR THE REPUBLICAN 80th CONGRESS	**$1000**	WHAT IS

DOUBLE JEOPARDY!

LAZYBONES

$200 WHAT IS (A) LOAFER? **$200**

$400 WHAT ARE ANTS? **$400**

$600 WHAT ARE IDLE HANDS? **$600**

$800 WHAT IS "SLACKER"? **$800**

$1000 WHAT IS DO-NOTHING? **$1000**

DOUBLE JEOPARDY!

FICTIONAL FOLKS

HUCK, AS IN HUCK FINN, IS SHORT FOR THIS	**$200**	WHAT IS
HE GAVE CHARLIE A TOUR OF HIS CHOCOLATE FACTORY	**$400**	WHO IS
1938 DAPHNE DU MAURIER NOVEL IN WHICH YOU FIND THE SECOND MRS. DE WINTER OF OUR DISCONTENT	**$600**	WHAT IS
THIS AUTHOR FELT HE HAD NO CHOICE BUT TO CREATE SOPHIE ZAWISTOWSKA	**$800**	WHO IS
A SINCLAIR LEWIS NOVEL ENDS WITH THIS PREACHER'S LINE "WE SHALL YET MAKE THESE UNITED STATES A MORAL NATION!"	**$1000**	WHO IS

DOUBLE JEOPARDY!™

FICTIONAL FOLKS

$200 WHAT IS HUCKLEBERRY? $200

$400 WHO IS WILLY WONKA? $400

$600 WHAT IS "REBECCA"? $600

$800 WHO IS WILLIAM STYRON? $800

$1000 WHO IS ELMER GANTRY? $1000

FINAL JEOPARDY!

THE COLD WAR

28 YEARS APART, THEY
ARE THE YEAR THE BERLIN
WALL ERECTED & THE YEAR
IT WAS TORN DOWN

WHAT ARE

FINAL JEOPARDY!

THE COLD WAR

WHAT ARE 1961 & 1989?

JEOPARDY!

HAIL TO THE CHIEF

Clue	Value	Response
IN 1974, AS GOVERNOR OF GEORGIA, HE APPEARED ON "WHAT'S MY LINE?" & STUMPED THE PANEL	**$100**	WHO IS
ISSUED IN 1862, A 10-DOLLAR NOTE DEPICTING HIM WAS THE FIRST U.S. CURRENCY TO FEATURE A LIVING PRESIDENT	**$200**	WHO IS
HE WAS BORN JAN. 30, 1882, IN HYDE PARK, NEW YORK	**$300**	WHO IS
HE WAS HAPPIER BEING CHIEF JUSTICE THAN PRESIDENT, & PROBABLY HAPPIER STILL WITH A BIG SLICE OF PIE IN FRONT OF HIM	**$400**	WHO IS
HE CLAIMED THE SMEAR & SLANDER TACTICS OF THE 1828 ELECTION DROVE HIS WIFE RACHEL TO HER GRAVE	**$500**	WHO IS

JEOPARDY!™

HAIL TO THE CHIEF

$100	WHO IS JIMMY CARTER?	**$100**
$200	WHO IS ABRAHAM LINCOLN?	**$200**
$300	WHO IS FRANKLIN D. ROOSEVELT?	**$300**
$400	WHO IS WILLIAM HOWARD TAFT?	**$400**
$500	WHO IS ANDREW JACKSON?	**$500**

JEOPARDY!

BRIT LIT

Clue	Value	Response
SHE HAD HER LOVER & FUTURE HUSBAND PERCY EDIT HER FIRST NOVEL, "FRANKENSTEIN"	**$100**	WHO IS
HIS OWN DISASTROUS TRIP TO THE CONGO IN 1890 WAS THE BASIS FOR HIS "HEART OF DARKNESS"	**$200**	WHO IS
HE WROTE ABOUT GUNGA DASS AS WELL AS GUNGA DIN	**$300**	WHO IS
IN 1816 SHE REVISED HER "NORTHANGER ABBEY"; SHE ORIGINALLY PLANNED TO PUBLISH IT IN 1803	**$400**	WHO IS
IN 1914's "THE WORLD SET FREE", HE WROTE OF A WAR IN 1958 INVOLVING ATOMIC BOMBS	**$500**	WHO IS

JEOPARDY!

BRIT LIT

$100	WHO IS MARY SHELLEY?	**$100**
$200	WHO IS JOSEPH CONRAD?	**$200**
$300	WHO IS RUDYARD KIPLING?	**$300**
$400	WHO IS JANE AUSTEN?	**$400**
$500	WHO IS H.G. WELLS?	**$500**

JEOPARDY!

SEAFOOD DIET

THE SOCKEYE SPECIES OF THIS FISH IS HIGHLY PRIZED FOR CANNING	**$100**	WHAT IS
PROBABLY THE FIRST FISH RAISED IN CAPTIVITY, THE RAINBOW SPECIES OF THIS FISH IS MOST COMMONLY FOUND ON FARMS	**$200**	WHAT IS
CALAMARI, ANOTHER NAME FOR THIS MOLLUSK WITH AN EDIBLE INK, COMES FROM THE LATIN FOR "WRITING PEN"	**$300**	WHAT IS
TOP QUALITY CAVIAR CONTAINS LESS THAN 5% OF THIS ADDITIVE	**$400**	WHAT IS
A METALWORKER WOULD KNOW THE NAME OF THIS SMALL, SILVERY FISH USUALLY FRIED & EATEN WHOLE	**$500**	WHAT IS

JEOPARDY!™

SEAFOOD DIET

$100	WHAT IS THE SALMON?	**$100**
$200	WHAT IS THE TROUT?	**$200**
$300	WHAT IS THE SQUID?	**$300**
$400	WHAT IS SALT?	**$400**
$500	WHAT IS THE SMELT?	**$500**

JEOPARDY!™

ANAGRAMMED COUNTRIES

TANGO	**$100**	WHAT IS
LIZ BRA	**$200**	WHAT IS
PAL DON	**$300**	WHAT IS
GOON MAIL	**$400**	WHAT IS
SAND HOUR	**$500**	WHAT IS

JEOPARDY!™

ANAGRAMMED COUNTRIES

$100　WHAT IS TONGA?　$100

$200　WHAT IS BRAZIL?　$200

$300　WHAT IS POLAND?　$300

$400　WHAT IS MONGOLIA?　$400

$500　WHAT IS HONDURAS?　$500

JEOPARDY!™

ACTORS IN HITCHCOCK FILMS

Clue	Value	Response
A GOOD GUY AS PERRY MASON, HE PLAYED THE BAD GUY JIMMY STEWART SPIED ON IN "REAR WINDOW"	$100	WHO IS
BEFORE HE PLAYED TED BAXTER, TED KNIGHT HAD A BIT ROLE AS A COP GUARDING NORMAN BATES IN THIS 1960 FILM	$200	WHAT IS
SUZANNE PLESHETTE IS FOUND PECKED TO DEATH IN THIS 1963 CLASSIC	$300	WHAT IS
FILM IN WHICH ROBERT WALKER PROPOSES A BLOODY BARGAIN TO FARLEY GRANGER WHILE TRAVELING	$400	WHAT IS
DIANE LADD KNOWS THIS ACTOR, HER EX-HUSBAND, APPEARED AS A SAILOR IN "MARNIE"	$500	WHO IS

JEOPARDY!™

ACTORS IN HITCHCOCK FILMS

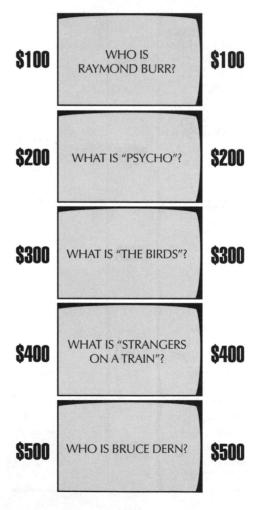

$100 — WHO IS RAYMOND BURR? — **$100**

$200 — WHAT IS "PSYCHO"? — **$200**

$300 — WHAT IS "THE BIRDS"? — **$300**

$400 — WHAT IS "STRANGERS ON A TRAIN"? — **$400**

$500 — WHO IS BRUCE DERN? — **$500**

JEOPARDY!

SKIN DEEP

Clue	Value	Response
WRINKLES AT THE CORNER OF THE EYE, PERHAPS CAUSED BY SQUINTING WHILE BIRDWATCHING	**$100**	WHAT ARE
THE COASTERS MIGHT KNOW CONTACT DERMATITIS CAN BE THE RESULT OF CONTACT WITH THIS PLANT	**$200**	WHAT IS
THE LITTLE SECTIONS OF DEAD EPIDERMIS AROUND YOUR FINGERNAILS	**$300**	WHAT ARE
THIS TERM FOR A BALM FOR THE SKIN OR THE CONSCIENCE GOES BACK TO THE SANSKRIT SARPIS, "MELTED BUTTER"	**$400**	WHAT IS
THE SKIN'S 2 EXOCRINE TYPES OF GLANDS ARE SWEAT GLANDS & THESE, WHICH PRODUCE OILS	**$500**	WHAT ARE

JEOPARDY!™

SKIN DEEP

$100	WHAT ARE CROW'S FEET?	**$100**
$200	WHAT IS POISON IVY?	**$200**
$300	WHAT ARE CUTICLES?	**$300**
$400	WHAT IS SALVE?	**$400**
$500	WHAT ARE SEBACEOUS GLANDS?	**$500**

DOUBLE JEOPARDY!

BROOKLYN NEIGHBORHOODS

IN 1968 THIS AREA CALLED "BED-STUY" ELECTED SHIRLEY CHISHOLM, THE FIRST BLACK WOMAN IN CONGRESS	**$200**	WHAT IS
CREATED IN 1903, LUNA PARK IN THIS AMUSEMENT AREA WAS SORT OF AN EARLY VERSION OF FANTASYLAND	**$400**	WHAT IS
A STREET GANG IN A 1974 FILM WAS CALLED "THE LORDS OF" THIS LARGE BROOKLYN NEIGHBORHOOD	**$600**	WHAT IS
AS THE SETTING FOR "THE HONEY-MOONERS", THIS AREA IN SW BROOKLYN COULD BE CALLED KRAMDENHURST	**$800**	WHAT IS
THESE "HEIGHTS" POPULATED BY AFRICAN-AMERICANS & HASIDIC JEWS WERE THE SITE OF RIOTING IN 1991	**$1000**	WHAT IS

DOUBLE JEOPARDY!

BROOKLYN NEIGHBORHOODS

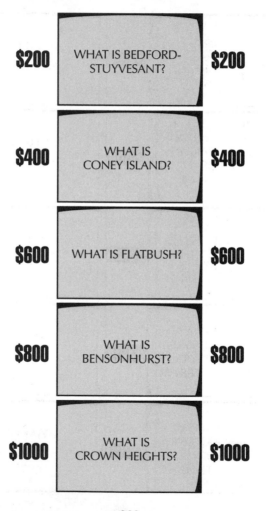

$200 — WHAT IS BEDFORD-STUYVESANT? — $200

$400 — WHAT IS CONEY ISLAND? — $400

$600 — WHAT IS FLATBUSH? — $600

$800 — WHAT IS BENSONHURST? — $800

$1000 — WHAT IS CROWN HEIGHTS? — $1000

DOUBLE JEOPARDY!

TALES TO TELL

Clue	Value	Response
IN 1851 HE PUBLISHED LITERATURE'S BEST-KNOWN WHALE TALE	**$200**	WHO IS
ARTHUR C. CLARKE FOLLOWED HIS BOOK "THE NINE BILLION NAMES OF GOD" WITH THIS OTHER NUMERICALLY TITLED TALE	**$400**	WHAT IS
BE THANKFUL WE'RE NOT GOING TO LIST ALL THE CHARACTERS IN HIS "GRAVITY'S RAINBOW"; THERE ARE OVER 400	**$600**	WHO IS
THIS 1993 ROBERT ALTMAN FILM WAS BASED ON A FEW TALES OF RAYMOND CARVER	**$800**	WHAT IS
THE UPSHOT IS HE WON THE HOWELLS MEDAL FOR HIS "WAPSHOT SCANDAL"	**$1000**	WHO IS

DOUBLE JEOPARDY!

TALES TO TELL

$200   WHO IS HERMAN MELVILLE?   **$200**

$400   WHAT IS "2001: (A SPACE ODYSSEY)"?   **$400**

$600   WHO IS THOMAS PYNCHON?   **$600**

$800   WHAT IS "SHORT CUTS"?   **$800**

$1000   WHO IS JOHN CHEEVER?   **$1000**

DOUBLE JEOPARDY!

. . . "UM"

IT HOLDS TWICE AS MUCH AS THE USUAL WINE OR CHAMPAGNE BOTTLE	**$200**	WHAT IS
IT'S A FINAL DEMAND OR STATEMENT OF CONDITIONS; DON'T MAKE ME GIVE YOU ONE	**$400**	WHAT IS
IT'S THE CLEAR, THIN PART OF THE BLOOD THAT REMAINS AFTER CLOTTING	**$600**	WHAT IS
HYDROGEN IS THE ONLY CHEMICAL ELEMENT THAT'S LIGHTER THAN THIS ONE	**$800**	WHAT IS
HE ALSO SCULPTED THE HEAD OF ABRAHAM LINCOLN FOR THE CAPITOL ROTUNDA	**$1000**	WHO IS

DOUBLE JEOPARDY!

..."UM"

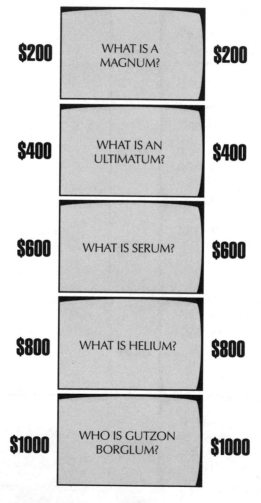

$200   WHAT IS A MAGNUM? $200

$400   WHAT IS AN ULTIMATUM? $400

$600   WHAT IS SERUM? $600

$800   WHAT IS HELIUM? $800

$1000   WHO IS GUTZON BORGLUM? $1000

DOUBLE JEOPARDY!

THE POLICE

SIR ROBERT PEEL ORGANIZED THIS CITY'S POLICE FORCE IN 1829 & THEY'VE BEEN NICKNAMED FOR HIM EVER SINCE	**$200**	WHAT IS
THIS WORD FOR A FRENCH POLICEMAN COMES FROM AN OLDER WORD MEANING PEOPLE-AT-ARMS	**$400**	WHAT IS
THEY WERE ONCE CALLED THE NORTH-WEST MOUNTED POLICE; NOW THEY PROTECT THE NORTH-WEST TERRITORIES	**$600**	WHAT IS
THIS COUNTRY'S CARABINIERI EVOLVED FROM A MILITARY GROUP THAT SERVED THE SAVOYARD STATES	**$800**	WHAT IS
THE NATIONAL POLICE FORCES OF ABOUT 180 COUNTRIES ARE MEMBERS OF THIS COOPERATIVE ORGANIZATION	**$1000**	WHAT IS

DOUBLE JEOPARDY!

THE POLICE

$200	WHAT IS LONDON?	**$200**
$400	WHAT IS A GENDARME?	**$400**
$600	WHAT IS THE ROYAL CANADIAN MOUNTED POLICE?	**$600**
$800	WHAT IS ITALY?	**$800**
$1000	WHAT IS INTERPOL?	**$1000**

DOUBLE JEOPARDY!

LOOK!

OPERATION LIFESAVER ENCOURAGES DRIVERS TO "LOOK, LISTEN AND LIVE!" WHEN CROSSING THESE	**$200**	WHAT ARE
IF YOU HEAR THIS SHOUT ON A GOLF COURSE, LOOK UP FOR INCOMING GOLF BALLS	**$400**	WHAT IS
IT MEANS TO TAKE A QUICK LOOK, OR TO HIT SOMETHING AT AN ANGLE & BOUNCE OFF	**$600**	WHAT IS
IF YOU'RE STARING AT SOMEONE, YOU MAY BE ADVISED TO DO THIS— "IT'LL LAST LONGER"	**$800**	WHAT IS
LOOKOUT MOUNTAIN JUST SOUTH OF THIS SOUTHERN TENNESSEE CITY OFFERS TOURISTS A VIEW OF 7 STATES	**$1000**	WHAT IS

DOUBLE JEOPARDY!

LOOK!

$200 — WHAT ARE RAILROAD TRACKS? — $200

$400 — WHAT IS FORE!? — $400

$600 — WHAT IS TO GLANCE? — $600

$800 — WHAT IS TAKE A PICTURE? — $800

$1000 — WHAT IS CHATTANOOGA? — $1000

DOUBLE JEOPARDY!

OFF THE AIR

THIS SITCOM WAS WELL INTO ITS FIRST SEASON WHEN JALEEL WHITE JOINED IT AS STEVE URKEL	**$200**	WHAT IS
FRIENDS OF THIS JAMES GARNER CHARACTER INCLUDED LAWYER BETH, POLICE DETECTIVE DENNIS & A PONTIAC FIREBIRD	**$400**	WHO IS
BOB NEWHART & THIS "TAXI" STAR TEAMED UP FOR "GEORGE & LEO", DESCRIBED AS "MORE GRUMPIER OLD MEN"	**$600**	WHO IS
IN THE EARLY '60s MARTIN MILNER & GEORGE MAHARIS GOT THEIR KICKS ON THIS SERIES	**$800**	WHAT IS
STARTING IN 1974 BERT CONVY HOSTED THIS GAME SHOW THAT FEATURED CELEBRITY COUPLES	**$1000**	WHAT IS

DOUBLE JEOPARDY!

OFF THE AIR

$200 | WHAT IS "FAMILY MATTERS"? | $200

$400 | WHO IS JIM ROCKFORD? | $400

$600 | WHO IS JUDD HIRSCH? | $600

$800 | WHAT IS "ROUTE 66"? | $800

$1000 | WHAT IS "TATTLETALES"? | $1000

FINAL JEOPARDY!
20th CENTURY NAMES

IN 1916, HIS VERY
PERSISTENT ASSASSINS
INCLUDED A PRINCE
& A GRAND DUKE

WHO IS

FINAL JEOPARDY!™

20th CENTURY NAMES

WHO IS RASPUTIN?